A CAVALCADE OF WITCHES

A CAVALCADE OF

witches

EDITED BY
JACYNTH HOPE-SIMPSON

ILLUSTRATED BY
KRYSTYNA TURSKA

NEW YORK
HENRY Z. WALCK, INCORPORATED

First published in Great Britain 1966
as THE HAMISH HAMILTON BOOK OF WITCHES

© 1966 Jacynth Hope-Simpson

Illustrations © 1966 Krystyna Turska

First American edition 1967

ISBN: 0–8098–2396–9

Library of Congress Catalog Card Number: AC 67–10163

Printed in Great Britain

To Elinor
who knows there are only White Witches
around the Red House

Contents

Acknowledgements

We wish to thank the agents, publishers and executors who granted permission to reprint the following works:

The Student-Witch from BEDKNOB AND BROOMSTICK, copyright, 1943, © 1957, by Mary Norton. Reprinted by permission of Harcourt, Brace & World, Inc., New York; and J. M. Dent & Sons Ltd., London.

Suppose You Met a Witch reprinted from BELINDA AND THE SWAN by Ian Serraillier, with permission of Jonathan Cape Ltd.

Zini and the Witches from RED INDIAN FOLK AND FAIRY TALES by Ruth Manning-Sanders, published by Oxford University Press Ltd., and reprinted by permission of David Higham Associates Ltd.

I Saw Three Witches and *The Little Creature* reprinted from COLLECTED RHYMES AND VERSES by Walter de la Mare, by permission of the Literary Trustees of Walter de la Mare and The Society of Authors as their representative.

The Boy on a Broomstick reprinted with permission of The Macmillan Company, New York, from THE MIDNIGHT FOLK by John Masefield. Copyright 1927, John Masefield, copyright renewed 1955 by John Masefield. Published in England by William Heinemann Ltd. and reprinted by permission of The Society of Authors and Dr. John Masefield, O.M.

Flying with Witches from FOLKTALES OF NORWAY, edited by Reidar Thorwald Christiansen, translated by Pat Shaw Iversen by permission of the University of Chicago Press. © The University of Chicago Press, 1964. Reprinted in England by permission of Routledge & Kegan Paul.

Baba Yaga and the Little Girl with the Kind Heart from OLD PETER'S RUSSIAN TALES by Arthur Ransome, reprinted by permission of Thomas Nelson & Sons Ltd.

ix

Some White Witchcraft from THE WITCHCRAFT AND FOLKLORE OF DARTMOOR by Ruth E. St. Leger-Gordon, reprinted by permission of Robert Hale Ltd.

Once In, Never Out Again from EUROPEAN FOLK TALES, reprinted by permission of Rosenkilde and Bagger, Copenhagen.

The Powers of Plants from A WITCH'S GUIDE TO GARDENING by Dorothy Jacob, reprinted by permission of Taplinger Publishing Co. Inc., New York, and Elek Books Ltd., London.

A Cat and a Broom from CARBONEL by Barbara Sleigh, reprinted by permission of Max Parrish Ltd.

Fereyel and Debbo Engal the Witch by Kathleen Arnott from AFRICAN MYTHS AND LEGENDS, reprinted by permission of Oxford University Press Ltd.

The Power of Thought from WITCHCRAFT TODAY by Gerald Gardner, reprinted by permission of Rider & Co.

The Queen of Underland reprinted in America with permission of The Macmillan Company from THE SILVER CHAIR by C. S. Lewis. Copyright 1953, The Macmillan Company. Reprinted in England by permission of Geoffrey Bles.

The Great-Aunt from SWALLOWDALE by Arthur Ransome, reprinted by permission of Jonathan Cape Ltd.

Lines Written in Dejection reprinted in America with permission of The Macmillan Company from COLLECTED POEMS by W. B. Yeats. Copyright 1919, The Macmillan Company, copyright renewed 1946 by Bertha Georgie Yeats. Reprinted in England by permission of M. B. Yeats, Esq., and Macmillan & Co. Ltd.

Introduction

Now o'er the one half-world
Nature seems dead, and wicked dreams abuse
The curtain'd sleep; now witchcraft celebrates
Pale Hecate's offerings. . . .

BUT. . . . "Are witches *real?*" asks a small child. He hugs his knees under the sheets, and pulls up the bedclothes around him so that only his eager, anxious eyes and the top of his head can be seen.

"No, of course not," replies his mother. "They're only something in stories. Lie down properly now, and I'll tuck you up."

"Only something in stories"—a strangely lasting "something in stories", for witch stories can be found again and again, all through history, all over the world. Hundreds of years before Christ, the poet whom we call Homer collected the lays that were sung about the heroes of Troy. He included amongst them the story of the witch, Circe. A mere hundred and fifty years ago, Jakob and Wilhelm Grimm started the modern work of collecting the stories that had been handed down, by word of mouth, from generation to generation. Their work of scholarship has become a classic source of stories for children. Among the most popular are the witch stories, like *Hansel and Gretel*. Nowadays, the ancient, entrancing art of telling stories aloud is in danger of dying out. Universities, bodies like the Council of Europe, promote the recording of folk tales before they are all forgotten. As we read these old stories, written down for the first time, we see, once again, how often the witch theme appears.

Homer turned Circe from a story told round the camp fire into an original work of great literature. Since his time, many other writers have written their variations upon the theme. The aim of this book is to show some of the many sides of writing about witches: folk tales, original stories, poems, historical records, legends. It is more concerned with the quality of the writing, and with providing variety, than with whether the contents fit any one theory about witchcraft. It does not add up to a theory on witchcraft itself.

xi

Why should the theme of witches appeal to so many writers and so many audiences? There is an almost mystical aspect: the magic of moonlight and lonely places, the sense we all have occasionally that something mysterious could happen if only we could detach ourselves from our humdrum lives. Within the last thousand years, something new has been added to the age-old belief in witches: the idea that they can fly. This has increased their hold on the imagination, for is not the longing to fly one of the most ancient of human dreams? Then there is the evil witch; the horrible, hateful, malevolent witch. She also appeals to something inside us. She can become a scapegoat for our sense that things are against us, and go wrong through no fault of our own. We all long to put everything straight, and emerge, triumphant and unharmed, like the hero of many a witch story.

"But," says the child again, "*are* witches real?" and we cannot evade his question. The answer that we would give depends greatly on who we are, and on when, in human history, we happen to live.

"Yes, of course they are real," an old nurse in ancient Athens might tell a child. "Everyone knows there are witches in Thessaly. Why, one night when a man was keeping watch over a corpse, some witches put a spell of sleep over him. Then they nibbled his nose and ears off, and put on wax ones instead." But the child's father, asked the same question, might only shrug his shoulders, for he had already rejected more important beliefs.

A child in the Middle Ages would have been given the answer, "Yes", but without any clear definition as to what witches were. If, as he grew up, he came to read the great writers of his time, Chaucer and Dante, he would have found little mention of witches. It was in the romances and ballads that the child would have come across strange creatures, half witch, half fairy, that influenced men's lives or led them, like Thomas the Rhymer, into mysterious lands.

> O they rade on, and farther on,
> And they waded rivers abune the knee;
> And they saw neither sun nor moon,
> But they heard the roaring of the sea.
>
> It was mirk, mirk night, there was nae starlight,
> They waded through red blude to the knee;
> For a' the blude that's shed on the earth
> Rins through the springs o' that countrie.

In the sixteenth and seventeenth centuries, the child would have had no doubt. Of course witches were real. Even the King, James I, had written a book about them, and who should know better than he? for some witches had plotted to kill him. Witches wove their spells on the London stage, in plays by writers like Ben Jonson.

3rd charm   The owl is abroad, the bat and the toad,
             And so is the cat-a-mountain;
             The ant and the mole both sit in a hole,
             And frog peeps out o' the fountain.
             The dogs they do bay, and the timbrels play,
             The spindle is now a-turning;
             The moon it is red, and the stars are fled,
             But all the sky is a-burning:
             The ditch is made, and our nails the spade:
             With pictures full, of wax and of wool,
             Their livers I stick with needles quick;
             There lacks but the blood to make up the flood.

There would have been another aspect of witchcraft that the child of the sixteenth and seventeenth centuries knew as he grew older: the searching for witches, the persecutions, the trials. In England the frenzy was less than in Scotland and parts of Europe, but still it is one of the ugliest episodes in our history. Even today the word "witch-hunt" is still used to describe a cruel persecution in which the victim is already almost condemned at the moment he is identified. Nor is what happened redeemed, as are the religious persecutions of the same time, by the spiritual inspiration of some of the victims themselves. If they had anything to testify to, they died silent.

It is not surprising that there should have been a reaction against this. By the end of the seventeenth century, still more in the eighteenth, educated Englishmen were sceptical about witches. At the most they would say, with Addison, "I believe in general that there is, and has been such a thing as Witchcraft; but at the same time can give no Credit to any particular Instance of it." To the enlightened liberals of the nineteenth century the whole thing was the product of ignorance and delusion.

And now—in the present day? We have learnt, thanks to Freud, that the human mind is far stranger than we had imagined. And we have learnt, thanks to Hitler, what it is like to live in a time of hatred and mass persecutions. We know what fantastic confessions can be dragged out of innocent

people. The twilight world of the witches has been, most bitterly, illumin-
ated for us.

That is why modern scholars writing about witchcraft are concerned less
with "whether?" than "what?" What did those people who claimed to be
witches do? Still more, *why* did they do it? Were they, as was once believed,
deliberately mocking the Christian faith and exalting Satan instead? Or were
they the relic of a more ancient cult? older than Christianity, older, too, than
the Greek gods of Olympus. Did they go back to the days when the supreme
principle worshipped was not the male but the female, in her triple aspect of
maiden, wife and old woman; the days when the moon was believed to have
greater powers than the sun? (Or, the outsider wonders, need the truth lie
exclusively one way or the other? In any case, did the witches themselves
always understand what they worshipped?)

And how about the people who claim to be witches today? Some of their
practices, if more fully revealed, might be of very great interest to those who
study how thoughts can be transmitted and shared. But this, to the world at
large, is rather an anticlimax, compared to a belief that witches had power
over the elements, to *untie the winds and let them fight*. It is further still from a
belief that ancient rites could ensure the due return of the seasons, the fertility
of the land, and of man, and beasts. Modern witchcraft seems to have shrunk
from a central, if sometimes forbidden, cult, to a "fringe" religion.

So, perhaps, we might tell the child that witches are most real when they
are imaginary. Then they become a symbol of power and of mystery. In the
last poem in this book, Yeats uses them in this way. If witches are banished,
he says,

> I have nothing but the embittered sun.

There are times when we all, adults and children alike, wish to retreat from
the sunlight. Here lies the enduring appeal of the witch theme to our minds.

> Light thickens; and the crow
> Makes wing to the rooky wood:
> Good things of day begin to droop and drowse
> While's night's black agents to their prey do rouse.

J.A.H.S.

The Student-Witch

MARY NORTON

How do you set about learning to be a witch? Mary Norton's suggestion is to take a correspondence course in the subject.

Miss Price was a very lady-like music teacher. When she sprained her ankle everybody believed she had fallen off her bicycle. Only Charles, Carey and Paul knew she had had an accident while learning to fly on a broomstick.

Mary Norton has a gift for clever, precise detail, which makes the fantastic seem credible, and which brings out the incongruity of this polite spinster learning to be a witch. The full adventures of Miss Price can be found in Bedknob and Broomstick. *The time of this story is the Second World War, as is revealed by the mention of "black-out shades". These were dark blinds drawn across a window so that no light would be shown to enemy aircraft.*

IT was about four o'clock in the afternoon when the children knocked at Miss Price's neat front door. The path on which they stood was gaily bordered with flowers and, through the half-open windows of the sitting-room, Miss Price's dimity curtains fluttered in the breeze. The door was opened by Agnes, a village girl who served Miss Price for a few hours daily.

As the children entered the little sitting-room, for a moment they felt very shy. There lay Miss Price on the sofa, her bandaged foot raised up on pillows. She still looked pale, but now her hair was tidy and her white blouse spotlessly neat.

"What lovely peaches! Thank you, my dears, and thank

your aunt. Very kind of her, I'm sure. Sit down, sit down."

The children sat down gingerly on the little spindly chairs.

"Agnes is making us some tea. You must stay and keep me company. Carey, can you open that card table?"

The children bustled round and helped to set the room for tea. A little table near Miss Price for the tea-tray and a white cloth on the card table for the scones, the bread and margarine, the quince jelly, and the ginger cake.

They enjoyed their tea and, when it was over, they helped Agnes to clear away. Then Miss Price showed Charles and Carey how to play backgammon and lent Paul a large book full of pictures called "Paradise Lost". Paul liked the book very much. He liked the musty smell of it and the gilt-edged pages.

When they had finished the game of backgammon and it seemed that it must be nearly time to go home, Carey took her courage in both hands.

"Miss Price," she said hesitatingly. "If it isn't rude to ask —are you a witch?"

There was silence for a moment, and Carey could feel her heart beating. Paul looked up from his book.

Very carefully, Miss Price closed the backgammon board and laid it on the little table beside the sofa. She took up her knitting and unfolded it.

"Well," she said slowly, "I am and I'm not."

Paul sat back on his heels. "You mean, you are sort of," he suggested.

Miss Price threw him a glance. "I mean, Paul," she said quietly, "that I am studying to be a witch." She knitted a few stitches, pursing up her mouth.

"Oh, Miss Price!" cried Carey warmly. "How terribly clever of you!"

It was the best thing she could have said. Miss Price flushed but she looked pleased.

"How did you first think of it, Miss Price?"

"Well, ever since I was a girl, I've had a bit of a gift for witchcraft, but somehow—what with piano lessons and looking after my mother—I never seemed to have the time to take it up seriously."

Paul was staring at Miss Price, as if to drink in every detail of her appearance. "I don't think you're a wicked witch," he said at last.

Miss Price dropped her eyes unhappily.

"I know, Paul," she admitted in a low voice. "You're quite right. I started too late in life. That's the whole trouble."

"Is being wicked the hardest part?" asked Carey.

"It is for me," Miss Price told her rather sadly. "But there are people who have a natural gift for it."

"Paul has," said Charles.

Paul came nearer and sat down on a chair. He was still staring at Miss Price, as if he longed to ask her something. After a minute, he found courage. "Could you just do a little bit of magic for us now?"

"Oh, Paul!" exclaimed Carey. "Don't worry Miss Price. She can't do magic with a sprained ankle."

"Yes, she could," protested Paul hotly. "She could do it lying down, couldn't you, Miss Price?"

"Well," said Miss Price, "I am a little tired, Paul. But I'll just do a little quick one and then you must all go home. There you are!"

Carey and Charles looked around quickly, following the direction of Miss Price's eyes. Paul's chair was empty. Paul had gone—but where he had been sitting perched a little yellow frog.

Before Carey or Charles had time to exclaim, Paul was back again, still staring expectantly at Miss Price.

"Oh," cried Carey, with a gasp, "That was wonderful, wonderful! How did you do it?"

She felt breathless and almost afraid. Magic—a spell—she had seen it with her own eyes.

"I didn't see anything," complained Paul.

Carey looked at him impatiently. "Oh, don't be silly, Paul. You turned into a frog. You must have felt it."

Paul's lips trembled. "I didn't feel anything," he said, in a squeaky little voice. But nobody heard him. Carey was staring at Miss Price with shining eyes.

"Miss Price," she pointed out almost reproachfully, "you could have done that at the church concert, instead of singing."

Miss Price laid down her knitting. A strange look crept into her face, and she looked hard at Carey as if she were seeing her for the first time. Nervously, Carey drew back in her chair.

"Although you sing so nicely," she added hastily.

But Miss Price did not seem to hear. There was a wild light in her eyes and her lips moved quietly, as if she were reciting. "There must be some way," she was saying slowly. "There-must-be-some-way. . . ."

"Some way of what?" asked Charles, after a moment's uncomfortable silence.

Miss Price smiled, showing her long yellow teeth.

"Of keeping your mouths shut," she rapped out.

Carey was shocked. This was far from lady-like. "Oh, Miss Price!" she exclaimed unhappily.

"Of keeping your mouths shut," repeated Miss Price slowly, smiling more unpleasantly than ever.

Paul made a little wriggling movement in his chair.

"Now she's getting wicked," he whispered to Carey in a pleased voice.

Carey drew away from him as if she had not heard. She looked worried. "What do you mean, Miss Price? You mean we mustn't tell anyone that—" She hesitated.

"That you're a witch?" put in Paul.

But Miss Price was still staring, as if she neither heard nor saw. "In just a minute I'll think of something," she said, as if to herself. "In just a minute. . . ."

Then Carey did something which Charles thought very brave. She got up from her chair and sat down beside Miss Price on the sofa.

"Listen, Miss Price," she said. "We did try to help you when you hurt your ankle. There isn't any need to use any kind of nasty magic on us. If you want to stop us telling, you could do it in a nice kind of way."

Miss Price looked at her. "How could I do it in a nice kind of way?" she asked, but she sounded more reasonable.

"Well," said Carey, "you could give us something— something magic—and if we told anyone about you, we'd have to forfeit it. You know, like a game. Directly we told, the thing would stop being magic."

"What sort of thing?" asked Miss Price, but as if the idea held possibilities.

Charles leaned forward. "Yes," he put in, "a ring or something, that we could twist and a slave comes. And, if we told about you, the slave wouldn't come any more. Couldn't you do that?"

Miss Price looked thoughtful. "I couldn't manage a slave," she said after a moment.

"Well, something like that."

Miss Price sat very quiet. She was thinking hard. "I know," she said, after a while. Suddenly, she seemed quite nice and cheerful again. "There's something I've been wanting to try out. Mind you, I'm not sure that it will work. Has anybody got a ring on them?"

Alas, none of them had. Paul felt in his pockets, just in case, but found nothing but the brass knob he had unscrewed from his bed that morning.

"Well, anything. A bracelet would do. It should be something you can twist."

But unfortunately, Carey could not produce a bracelet either. "I have one at home," she said, "but I only wear it on Sundays."

"You can twist this," cried Paul suddenly, holding out the bed-knob. "That's just what it does. It twists and it twists and it twists. I twisted it off," he added rather unnecessarily.

Miss Price took the bed-knob and held it thoughtfully between her clean, bony fingers.

"Let me see . . ." she said slowly. Then suddenly she looked up, as if surprised. "Paul, I believe this is the best thing you could have given me." (Paul squirmed, pleased but bashful.) "Now, I could do a wonderful spell with this —but I must think it out very carefully. Now, be quiet, children, and let me think—so that I can get this right." Her fingers closed gently round the shining brass. "This should be very good indeed. Now, quiet, please!"

The children sat like statues. Even Paul forgot to fidget. A bumble-bee came in through the window and buzzed heavily about the room. Except for this, the silence was complete.

After what seemed a long while, Miss Price opened her eyes. And then she sat up, blinking and smiling. "There you are, Paul," she said brightly, and handed him back the bed-knob.

He took it reverently. "Is it done?" he asked in an awe-stricken voice. It looked just the same to him.

"Yes, it's quite done," Miss Price told him. "And it's a very good spell indeed. This is something you'll enjoy. Only don't get yourselves into trouble."

Carey and Charles were looking enviously at Paul.

"What must we do with it?" asked Charles.

"Just take it home and screw it back on the bed. But don't screw it right up. Screw it about half-way."

"And then?"

"And then?" Miss Price smiled. "Twist it a little and wish—and the bed will take you to wherever you want to go!"

The children gazed unbelievingly at the gleaming ball in Paul's rather grubby fingers.

"Really?" asked Carey, with a little gasp.

Miss Price was still smiling. She seemed very pleased with herself. "Well, try it."

"Oh, Miss Price!" breathed Carey, still gazing at the knob. "*Thank you.*"

"Don't thank me," said Miss Price, taking up her knitting again. "Remember the conditions. One word about me and the spell is broken."

"Oh, Miss Price!" said Carey again. She was quite overcome.

"Well, now off you go. It's getting late. As I say, don't get yourselves into trouble and don't go gallivanting around all night. There should be moderation in all things —even in magic."

At about ten o'clock next morning, the children were back again. Their faces were serious and their manner uncertain.

"Could I . . ." said Carey to the cheerful Agnes, "could we see Miss Price?" She gave a little swallow, as if she felt nervous.

"Miss Price is engaged at the moment," replied Agnes. "Is there a message?"

"Well . . ." Carey hesitated. How much did Agnes know? She looked around at the others. Charles stepped forward.

"Could you just tell her," he said, "that it didn't work?"

"It didn't work?" repeated Agnes.

"Yes. Just say 'It didn't work.' "

"It didn't work," repeated Agnes to herself, as if memorizing the message. She disappeared down the passage, leaving the front door open. They heard her knock. Then, after a minute, Agnes returned.

"Miss Price says will you step in."

They were shown once more into the sitting-room. Each chose a chair and sat on the edge of it.

"I bet she'll be angry," whispered Paul, breaking the silence.

"Shush," said Carey. She looked a little pale.

Suddenly the door opened and Miss Price limped in. Her foot was bandaged and she wore a carpet slipper, but she was able to walk without a stick. She looked round from face to face. "It didn't work?" she said slowly.

"No," replied Carey, clasping her hands together in her lap.

Miss Price sat down in the centre of the sofa. They all stared at each other in silence.

"Are you sure you did it right?"

"Yes, just what you said. We half screwed it on. Then turned it a little and wished."

"And what happened?"

"Nothing," said Carey. Paul's eyes, round with accusation, were fixed on Miss Price's face.

"I can't understand it," said Miss Price, after a moment. She thought awhile. "Have you got it with you?" she asked.

Yes, Carey had it, in a checked sponge bag. Miss Price drew out the golden ball and gazed at it nonplussed.

"Didn't the bed move at all?"

"Only by Paul bouncing on it."

"It's rusty here at the bottom," said Miss Price.

"It was always like that," Carey told her.

"Well, I don't know." Miss Price stood up, gingerly putting her sprained foot to the floor. "I'll take it along and test it." She made a move towards the door.

"Could we watch you?"

Miss Price turned back slowly. The circle of eager eyes seemed to hold her. They saw her hesitate. "Please, Miss Price!" urged Carey.

"No one has seen my workroom," said Miss Price. "Not even Agnes."

Carey was going to say, "But we're in the secret," but she thought better of it and kept quite quiet. Their longing eyes spoke for all of them.

"Well, I'll just send Agnes off for the groceries and then I'll see."

She went out. And it seemed an eternity before she called them. Eagerly they ran out into the passage. Miss Price was putting on a white overall. In her hand was a key. They followed her down two or three steps into a short dark passage. They heard the key turn in a well-oiled lock. Miss Price went in first, then stood aside.

"Quietly," she said, beckoning them in. "And careful what you touch."

The room must at one time have been a larder. There were marble slabs and wooden shelves above the slabs. The first thing Carey noticed were the glass jars, each with its typewritten label. Miss Price, a spot of proud pink in each cheek, ran a hand along the rows.

"Toads, hares' feet, bats' wings—oh, dear!" She picked up an empty jar to which a few damp balls still clung. "I'm out of newts' eyes!" She peered into the jar before she stood it back upon the shelf, then, taking up a pencil, she made a note on a memo. pad which hung upon the wall. "They're almost impossible to get nowadays," she said with a sigh. "But we mustn't grumble. It's wartime. This is my little filing cabinet where I record results,

successful—and unsuccessful, too, I'm afraid. My note-
books. . . ."

Carey, leaning forward, saw these were stout exercise
books, neatly labelled.

"Spells . . . Charms . . . Incantations," she read aloud.

"And I don't suppose any of you know," said Miss Price
brightly, "the difference between a spell and a charm."

"I thought they were the same thing," said Charles.

"A-ha," replied Miss Price darkly, but her face was

alight with hidden knowledge. "I only wish a spell were as easy as a charm."

She lifted a spotless piece of butter muslin, and the children peered, not without a shudder, at what appeared to be a greenish slab of meat. It lay symmetrically in a gleaming, porcelain dish and smelt faintly of chemicals.

"What is it?" asked Carey.

Miss Price eyed the dish dubiously. "It's poisoned dragon's liver," she said uncertainly.

"Oh," said Carey politely.

Paul pushed up close. "Did you poison the dragon, Miss Price? Or just the liver?" he added.

"Well," admitted the truthful Miss Price, "as a matter of fact, it came ready prepared. It's part of the equipment."

"It all looks very hygienic," ventured Carey timidly.

"My dear Carey," said Miss Price reprovingly, "we have progressed a little since the Middle Ages. Method and prophylactics have revolutionized modern witchcraft."

Carey felt Miss Price was quoting from a book and she longed to know a little more. "Could I just see Lesson I?" she asked.

Miss Price glanced quickly at a pile of folders on an upper shelf and then she shook her head. "I'm sorry, Carey. This course is absolutely confidential. 'Any infringement of this regulation,'" she quoted, " 'entails a fine of not less than two hundred pounds and condemns the offender to chronic, progressively recurring, attacks of Cosmick Creepus.'"

Paul looked pensive. "It's cheaper to spit in a bus," he announced, after some seconds of silent thought.

Gradually, the children discovered other treasures: a chart on which the signs of the zodiac were nicely touched up by Miss Price in water-colour; a sheep's skull; a chocolate box full of dried mice; herbs in bunches; a pot of growing hemlock and one of witch's bane; a small stuffed alligator which hung by two wires from the ceiling.

"What are alligators used for, Miss Price?" asked Paul.

Again Miss Price's long training in truthfulness overcame her longing to impress. "Nothing much," she said. "They're out of date now. I like to have it here for the look of it."

"It does look nice," Paul agreed, rather enviously. He stuck his hands in his pockets. "I had a dead hen once," he added carelessly.

But Miss Price did not hear him. She was arranging three hazel twigs on a shelf in the form of a triangle. In the centre of this, she set the bed-knob.

"Now pass me that red note-book, just by your hand, Carey."

"The one marked 'Spells'?"

"Yes." Miss Price took it. She put on her spectacles and spent some time gazing at the open page. Picking up a pencil, she scribbled a few figures on a piece of shelf paper. She stared at these and then she rubbed them out with the other end of the pencil.

"Miss Price . . ." began Paul.

"Don't interrupt me," murmured Miss Price. "Hellebore, henbane, aconite . . . glow-worm fire and firefly light . . . Better pull down the black-out shades, Carey."

"The black-out shades, Miss Price?"

"Yes, over the window. Or we shan't be able to see this experiment."

Carey pulled down the shades and adjusted them. As the room became dark, Miss Price exclaimed, "Now, isn't that pretty!" She sounded surprised and delighted. The children crowded round her and saw that the bed-knob glowed with a gentle light—pale as early dawn. As they watched, Miss Price twisted the knob a little and the pale light turned to rose.

"There, you see!" Miss Price said triumphantly. "What's wrong with that, I'd like to know? Pull up the blinds again, Carey."

Carey rolled up the blind and hooked the black-out oil-cloth on its little hook. Miss Price slipped an elastic band round the three hazel twigs and tidied up the note-books.

"Come along," she said cheerfully, opening the door. "The spell works perfectly. Better than I hoped. I can't imagine where you went wrong."

They followed Miss Price up the stairs, down the passage, and out through the open door into the garden, where the air was sweet with the smell of sun-warmed earth. Butter-flies balanced precariously on the spears of lavender and bumble-bees hung in the foxglove bells. A milkman's cart stopped at the gate. There was a clang of bottles.

"Thank you ever so much," said Carey. "We'll try it again this evening. I did just what you said. I didn't screw it tight at all. I . . ."

"You?" said Miss Price. "You did it, Carey?"

"Yes. I did it myself. I was very careful. I . . ."

"But, Carey," said Miss Price, "I gave the spell to Paul."

"You mean Paul should've . . .?"

"Of course. Paul should have done it. No wonder it didn't work."

Slowly, wonderingly, a grin of ecstasy began to stretch itself across Paul's face. His eyes gleamed moistly with an almost holy joy.

Carey and Charles looked at him as though they had never seen him before.

"Well?" said Miss Price, rather sharply.

Charles found his voice. "He's sort of young," he pointed out, "for so much responsibility."

But Miss Price was firm. "The younger the better, as I know to my cost. Now run along, children." She turned away, but almost immediately she turned back again, lowering her voice: "Oh, by the way, I meant to tell you something else. You know I said the spell was better than I hoped. Well, if you twist it one way the bed will take you where you want, in the present. Twist it the other way and the bed will take you back into the past."

"Oh, Miss Price!" exclaimed Carey.

"What about the future?" asked Charles.

Miss Price looked at him as the bus conductor looks when you ask for a ticket to a place off the bus route. Charles blushed, and churned up the gravel path with the toe of his shoe.

"Now, remember what I said," went on Miss Price. "Have a good time, keep to the rules, and allow for the bed."

She turned to the milkman, who had been waiting patiently by the step. "Half a pint, please, Mr. Bisselthwaite, and my butter."

Suppose You Met a Witch

IAN SERRAILLIER

Well . . . suppose you did. Ian Serraillier shows the sort of things that might happen. He has taken a traditional theme (from Grimms' version of Hansel and Gretel) *and turned it into an original poem in a distinctively modern style. Neither the old nor the new appear out of place in this lively poem, which comes from* Belinda and the Swan.

Suppose you met a witch . . . There's one I know,
all willow-gnarled and whiskered head to toe.
We drownded her at Ten Foot Bridge
last June, I think,—
but I've often seen her since at twilight time
under the willows by the river brink,
skimming the wool-white meadow mist
astride her broom o' beech.
And once, as she flew past, with a sudden twist
and flick of the stick she whisked me in
head over heels, splash in the scummy water
up to my chin—
ugh! . . .
Yet there are witless folk will say
they don't exist.
But I was saying— suppose *you* met a witch,
up in that murky waste of wood
where you play your hide and seek. Suppose

she pounced from out a bush,
she touched you, she clutched you,
what would you do? No use
in struggling, in vain to pinch and pull.
She's pinned you down, pitched you into her sack,
drawn tight the noose.

There's one way
of escape, one word you need to know—
W—A—N—D. Well,
What does that spell? . . .
They learnt it years ago,
two children—Roland and Miranda—clapped
in a witch's sack and trapped
just as you might be. *He*
was a mild and dreamy boy, musical
as a lark—in the dark
of the jolting sack he sang. *She*
was quick in all she did, a nimble wit, her brain
busy as a hive of bees at honey time.

And Grimblegrum—that was the witch's name—
jogged them home.

This was the usual sort, a candy villa
with walls of gingerbread, porch and pillar
of barley sugar. She kicked the gate
and the licorice-beaded door,
undid the sack string and tipped them
on the glassy glacier-minted floor.
As Roland fell, his boot struck
the crystal paving stones and chipped them.
Like an angry rocket

she launched at him. Miranda
sprang for the magic wand
and pinched it from her pocket.
        "Tip, tap—O house of cake,
        be a cloud-reflecting lake
        with me and Roland, each a swan,
        gracefully afloat thereon!
        And, deeper than e'er plummet sounded
        Grimblegrum the witch be drownded!"

'Twas done—look there, d'you see two swans
a-gliding, serene and cool
upon that heaven-painted pool,
over the blue sky, over the floating clouds that shine
like snow-white fleeces?
Sudden, in burst of bubbles the witch popped up
and shivered the cloud to pieces.

"I'll gobble you yet!" she gulped,
but all she gobbled was water as with windmill arms
she thrashed and lashed at them. No swimmer,
she would have sunk like a boulder below,
had not a felon crow,
black-hearted as his feather, swooping, dipping,
hoisted her by the belt and borne her, boggy,
drooping, dripping,
home.
        "She'll follow us—no time to lose—
quick we must fly!" Miranda cried.
Heavily they rose;
far over field and forest, with whining wing
all night through
till dawn of day they flew.

Meanwhile the Grimble-witch, now dry,
had put on her seven league boots and (do or die)
seven mile at a step came galloping,
gulping, "Gobble you yet, I'll gobble you yet!"

The swans heard her cackle and a thudding where she
    stepped—
down by a screen of trees they swept,
down to a lonely roadside out of view.

"I'll change myself to a rose of crimson hue,
set in a prickly hedge," Miranda said,
"and, Roland, as for you,
you'll be a piper, and the magic wand
your flute."

Not a second too soon—for the witch's boot
touched ground beside them. And she croaked:

"O glorious goriest rose!
I have sought you from afar,
how I wonder what you are!
You may mock me from on high,
but I'm the spider, you're the fly!
Ha! ha! ha! ha! ha! ha!"

And she gaped at that glorious and goriest of roses
with the greediest of eyes and the nosiest of noses.
Again she spoke:
"Good piper, this rose how dainty it would look
if I stuck it in my cloak!
May I pluck it?"
            "Good lady, you may. And I'll play
to you the while." And Roland smiled,
for his was a *magic* flute,
each golden note entrancing—
none could listen without dancing.

            One note one,
                she spun like a top.

            Two notes two,
                she hopped and couldn't stop

> Three notes three—
> and into that thorny thistle-y tree
> with a hop, skip and a jump went she.

Tootle-toot! sang the flute
and up went her boot
and down again soon
to the tantivy tune.
Every thorn and twig
did dance to the jig
and the witch willy-nilly—
each prickle and pin
as it skewered her in
was driving her silly.

Hi!
   ho!
      shrieked she,
and *tickle-me-thistle!* and *prickle-me-dee!*
and battered she was as she trotted and tripped,
and her clothes were all torn and tattered and ripped
till at last,
all mingled and mangled,
  her right leg entangled,
    her left leg right-angled,
firm as a prisoner pinned to the mast,
she
  stuck
   fast.

Silence, not a sound as Roland wiped
the sweat from his brow. Then gently with his pipe
he touched the rose. Out leapt Miranda

to the ground. Hand in hand,
chuckling, through the wild wood
away home they ran.

That same evening, a cowman passing by
paused by a roadside bush to cut a switch.
He heard a cry;
turning, saw in a hedge nearby a prickly witch
who screamed and yelled and hissed at him and spat.

So he put a match to the hedge. And that was that.

Zini and the Witches

RUTH MANNING-SANDERS

This very individual story from Red Indian Folk and Fairy Tales *has many changes of mood, from the eerie cave of the witches to the enchanting Baby Squirrel, who can only dance properly when someone is watching him.*

THERE was once a young Brave, called Zini, who married a woman from a far-away tribe. She had a very beautiful voice, and every night she would sing Zini to sleep, but always the songs were in a language he did not understand.

One night he said to her, "What are those songs that you sing to me, my wife?"

"Sleepy songs," she answered, "the ancient songs of my people."

"I wish I might know what the words mean," said Zini. And she answered, "This is what they mean:

'Go to sleep, my darling, my love,
Go to sleep, my darling.
Sleep soundly, sleep soundly, my darling, my love,
Go to sleep, my darling.
Sleep till dawn wakes you, my darling, my love,
Go to sleep, my darling!'"

"Oh, is that what they mean?" said Zini.
"Yes," said she. "What else should they mean?"

But Zini was puzzled. It seemed to him that the songs didn't sound quite like that. He was so puzzled that he dreamed he was caught in a monstrous spider's web, and then he woke up.

"Sing me to sleep again, my wife," he said.

But there was no answer. His wife had gone.

In the morning she was back again by his side. He thought he would ask her where she had been; and then he thought he wouldn't. Instead, he went to the Medicine Man, and told him.

The Medicine Man shook his head. "I fear she has taken the wrong road," he said.

By which he meant she wasn't good but bad.

He told Zini to look all round the house when his wife was out, especially in places where it was dark.

When Zini got home, his wife was just coming out with a brightly painted jar on her head. She was going to the spring for water. The spring was some way off. Zini thought now was his chance to look round the house, and to save time he decided to look in the dark places first. He looked in one dark place and saw nothing. And he looked in another dark place and saw nothing. And then he lifted a curtain to look in a third dark place, and he saw—it isn't easy to say what he saw. There were bodies and bones, and all sorts of horrors. So then Zini knew his wife was a witch.

He went off to the Medicine Man again, and this time he was crying.

"You must keep awake to-night," said the Medicine Man, and he gave Zini a little red seed. "Put this on your tongue and you won't go to sleep, let her sing as long as she will. But you must pretend to sleep, and then watch what happens, and come to me again."

So that night Zini put the little red seed on his tongue

before he went to bed. His wife began to sing to him, and he yawned and sighed and closed his eyes, but he was wide, wide awake. His wife was a little bit suspicious—perhaps he wasn't breathing quite right for a sleeping man. At any rate she sang much longer than usual.

By and by a big black cat came creeping in and stood at the top of the steps.

"We are all waiting for you," whispered the cat. "Why don't you come?"

"You must wait for me a little while," said the wife. "The man is stirring in his sleep."

Then Zini lay very, very still. He breathed gently and evenly—he even snored a little.

By and by a big grey owl flew down through the smoke hole. "You must hurry," whispered the owl, "the Chief is getting angry."

The wife looked at Zini. "He is asleep now," she said, and she tiptoed away and climbed the ladder out of the house.

Zini got up and followed her, keeping in the shadows. It was a bright moonlight night, and though he kept at a distance he could see her moving from the shadows into the light and back into the shadows again. He followed her till they came to a black mountain. At the bottom of the mountain was a big, dark cave. The mouth of the cave was dripping with water, and the moon shone on the water and turned it into a white rainbow. The wife passed under the white rainbow, and as she did so she became a pink cat.

Zini stood under the rainbow and peered into the cave.

There was a fire blazing in the middle of the cave, and witches were flying in through the walls. As they alighted on the floor they turned into animals and birds, vultures

and wolves and lynxes and owls and cats. Behind the fire the Witch Chief sat on a throne. The throne was a huge bat, and the Chief sat between its wings. The bat had its head down, and the Chief used its head as a footstool. The bat didn't look at all comfortable, but when it tried to move, the Chief kicked it, and then it was still again.

"You are very late," said the Witch Chief to the pink cat; and he gave her four scratches with his long nails, two scratches on her face, and two on her chest.

"I can't help it," said the pink cat angrily, "my husband is getting to suspect me. He asked me what my songs meant, but I fooled him."

And she told the Chief what she had said to Zini.

"And what do the words of the song really mean?" asked the Witch Chief.

"What do they mean?" said the pink cat. "This is what they mean:

> 'Go to sleep, you horrible man,
> Go to sleep, you horror.
> Sleep soundly, sleep soundly, you horrible man,
> Go to sleep, you horror.
> Sleep till I wake you, you horrible man,
> Go to sleep, you horror.' "

"Ha! Ha! Ha!" laughed the Witch Chief. And "Ha! Ha! Ha!" laughed all the vultures and wolves and lynxes and owls and cats. Then they looked up and saw Zini peeping in under the white rainbow.

Zini tried to run away, but they rushed at him and dragged him into the cave. They tied his hands behind his back and stood him before the Chief.

"You deserve to die for this," said the Chief. "But I will spare your life on one condition. Bring me the hearts of your mother and sister and you shall live. Not only shall you live, but you shall become one of us. We will turn you into a mighty witch, and you shall help your wife to work evil." Then he ordered the creatures to free Zini's arms, and told him to go home. "To-morrow night I shall expect you again, with your offering of hearts," he said. "If you do not come, I shall see to it that your wife skins you alive."

Zini didn't go home, he went to the Medicine Man and told him what had happened.

"This is terrible," said the Medicine Man. "I scarcely know what we can do." He thought for a long time, and

then he said, "You will have to go back to the cave
to-morrow night, that is certain. But you cannot cut out
the hearts of your mother and sister. You must kill two
sheep and carry their hearts to the Witch Chief. We may
be able to deceive him, but I doubt it." The Medicine Man
shook his head, and shook his head. "I fear trouble will
come of it," he said.

Then he gave Zini a little red shell, and told him to hide
it in the folds of his shirt. "It will at least protect your life,
if it will do no more," he said.

So Zini hid the little red shell in the folds of his shirt, and
he went home and killed two sheep. His wife didn't come
home all that day, and he was glad rather than sorry.
When night came, he wrapped the two sheeps' hearts in a
napkin made of cat-tail reeds and carried them to the cave.

The Witch Chief was there, sitting behind the fire on
his bat-throne, and the pink cat was there, and all the other
creatures. They were having a feast, taking all sorts of
unpleasant things out of a big oven, and swallowing everything down smoking hot.

"I have brought you the hearts," said Zini to the Chief.
He was as frightened as could be, but he was trying not to
show it.

The Chief told the pink cat to put the hearts in the oven.
By and by they began to sizzle.

"Ba-a-a-a!" they said.

"Was your mother a sheep, and was your sister a sheep?"
said the Witch Chief.

"Of course not," answered Zini. "But they had a sheep
for their totem." He had to say something, and that was
the first thing he thought of.

The Chief pretended to be satisfied with his explanation,
and he told Zini to go home and lie down to sleep.

It seemed to Zini that he did go home, but that was only the Witch Chief's magic. When Zini woke in the morning, he found himself lying on a ledge of rock. The ledge was half-way up a great cliff. Below the ledge, the cliff went down for a thousand feet, as steep and straight as a house wall; and above the ledge, the cliff rose up another thousand feet, equally steep and straight, and there wasn't a crack or a crevice anywhere in the cliff that a man could climb up or down by.

The ledge was only just wide enough to take Zini's body, and he couldn't move backwards or forwards or sideways. He was lying on his back, and the sun was beating down on his head. He lay there all day without moving, and when night came it was bitterly cold, and his shirt froze to the ledge. And when morning came, the sun beat down on him again, and he felt he was being roasted alive. He didn't die, because the little red shell in the fold of his shirt kept him alive, but he suffered from heat and cold and hunger and thirst and giddiness, and he almost felt that it would be better if he could die.

When the sun was high on the third day, a baby squirrel came hoppity-skip along the ledge. He saw Zini's moccasins sticking up and climbed on to one of them. Then he sat down and wrinkled his nose and looked along Zini's body as far as his face. Zini's eyes were closed, he didn't even seem to be breathing.

"Nana! Nana!" called Baby Squirrel, "I've found a dead man on our ledge!"

Then Mother Squirrel came along, hoppity-skip, hoppity-skip; and she climbed on to Zini's other moccasin and looked along his body to his face. Zini opened his eyes and stared at the sky, and then he shut his eyes again.

"He's not dead," said Mother Squirrel, "but I think he's

starving." She took an acorn cup out of her cheek. "Here, son," she said to Baby Squirrel, "fill this with corn meal and water."

Baby Squirrel took the acorn cup, jumped down off Zini's moccasin, and went off, hoppity-skip, hoppity-skip. In less than no time he was back again, with the cup filled with wet corn meal.

Mother Squirrel took the cup from him, and ran hoppity-skip, hoppity-skip, all the way along Zini's body till she came to his face.

"Eat!" she said.

Zini raised his neck, very stiffly, and looked down at the acorn cup. Then he gave a very small smile and shook his head. It was kind of Mother Squirrel, but what good would a tiny lick of corn meal like that be to him?

"Eat! Eat!" said Mother Squirrel, holding the acorn cup to his lips. "You must eat to get strong. It may look a little, but it's more than enough."

So then, to please her, Zini ate the wet corn meal. He ate and ate, and still the acorn cup was full. He ate until he could eat no more, and then he gave a big smile and said, "Thank you!"

"Feeling better?" said Mother Squirrel.

"Much, much better," said Zini.

Hoppity-skip, hoppity-skip, Mother Squirrel went off and came back with a cedar branch. This she laid over Zini's head to protect him from the sun. And when night came she was back again, hoppity-skip, with a bark-fibre blanket, and this she laid over him to protect him from the cold.

Three times a day Baby Squirrel brought him the acorn cup full of wet corn meal, and between whiles he sat on Zini's moccasin and told him stories and danced. He did a War Dance, and a Buffalo Hunt Dance, and the Sun Dance, and the Dance to Scare Away False Faces That Look At You Out of The Trees. He danced every dance he knew.

"But you must watch me," he said to Zini. "I can't dance properly if you don't."

So Zini lifted up his neck and watched Baby Squirrel strutting around on his moccasin, and stamping.

"Ha! Ha! Yahi-yahi! Yeh!" shouted Baby Squirrel.

"Ha! Ha! Yahi-yahi! Yoh!" answered Zini, and that pleased Baby Squirrel mightily.

Zini even managed to clap his hands now and then. He was feeling ever so much stronger.

Mother Squirrel was busy doing something else. She went to her store-place and fetched a pine cone. Then she came and stood at Zini's feet, and dropped the pine cone over the cliff. The pine cone fell down, down, a thousand feet down. Mother Squirrel peeped over the edge and watched it falling.

"Grow, grow, pine cone grow! Grow, grow, grow!" she said.

In the morning, after Baby Squirrel had brought him his breakfast, Zini felt so much stronger that he was able to sit up. He raised himself very, very carefully, so as not to topple sideways, and then he too peered over the edge. Down, down, a thousand feet down, he saw a great plain with green grass and a river, and close against the cliff a little pine tree was growing. When he looked again in the evening, the little pine was a tall tree, and when he looked again next morning, its topmost branches reached half-way up the cliff. Every time he looked at it, it had grown taller; by the fourth morning its topmost branches were on a level with the ledge, and by the fourth evening it towered,

strong and mighty, high above his head, and a great branch
of it lay against the ledge close to Zini's hand.

Hoppity-skip! Mother Squirrel was dancing on the
branch. "Now, friend Zini," she said, "it's time to go
home. Take hold of the branch and follow me."

Hoppity-skip! Baby Squirrel jumped on to Zini's
shoulder; Zini grasped the branch with both hands and
swung himself off the ledge. Hoppity-skip! Mother Squirrel was dancing on the branch just below. Zini swung himself on to that branch, and so they went, down, down, a
thousand feet down, till they stood side by side on the
plain.

"Now, friend Zini, it's time to say good-bye," said
Mother Squirrel. "Follow the river, and you'll soon get
home."

Zini thanked her and thanked her. "Pooh!" said Mother
Squirrel, "it would be a poor world if we couldn't do that
much for each other!" Then she gave him some pine tree
seeds and some pinyon nuts. "When you get home," she
said, "give your wife the pine seeds, but you yourself must
eat the pinyon nuts. Now remember—pine seeds for her,
pinyon nuts for you. It's very important."

Zini said he would remember, and thanked her again.
Then they said good-bye to each other. Mother Squirrel
and Baby Squirrel climbed back up the tree, and Zini went
along by the river and found himself back in his own
village.

His wife was very surprised to see him. "Why," said she,
"I thought you were dead! You've been away four years,
and now I've married another man."

"Poor fellow!" thought Zini. But he was glad to know
that she wasn't his wife any more. He went in and talked
pleasantly to the new husband. The poor man looked

scared; he grasped Zini by the hand and said he was very glad he had come back.

"Oh, I've brought you some pine seeds," said Zini to his wife and she took them and ate them, and Zini and the new husband shared the pinyon nuts between them. After that, the new husband made up a bed on the floor for Zini, and the wife sang them both to sleep. Early in the morning Zini and the new husband went out hunting together, and the wife busied herself about the house.

"I shan't expect you back till sunset," she said to the men.

Zini wondered if they would ever come back; but he said nothing, and the new husband said nothing. Each of them shot a fine fat buck; and towards sunset, not knowing what else to do, they returned to the village.

But when they drew near their house they stopped and stared. The wicked wife had vanished, and in her place, pushing up through the roof, and growing high above it, was a great pine tree. Its dark branches were thrust out through the sides of the house, and they were waving about like arms, as if they were trying to catch hold of something. But there was nothing to catch hold of, and from the pine tree came a mighty sighing, like waves on a far-off shore. Sometimes the sighing grew louder, and sometimes it grew softer, but it never stopped.

And it will never stop as long as that pine lives.

By and by the pine grew so big that it cracked the walls round it, and the house fell down in pieces. But Zini and the new husband built themselves another house, where they lived together like good friends. They went hunting together, and they went fishing together; and after a bit they married two sisters, who were both good women, and they all four lived happily for the rest of their lives.

Two Poems

WALTER DE LA MARE

Walter de la Mare, who died in 1956, has a unique place among writers of this century for his power to evoke a dream-like world that seems to be on the edge of memory; as if he were writing about something that we had once experienced but had almost completely forgotten.

I SAW THREE WITCHES

I saw three witches
That bowed down like barley,
And took to their brooms 'neath a louring sky,
And, mounting a storm-cloud,
Aloft on its margin,
Stood black in the silver as up they did fly.

I saw three witches
That mocked the poor sparrows
They carried in cages of wicker along,
Till a hawk from his eyrie
Swooped down like an arrow,
And smote on the cages, and ended their song.

I saw three witches
That sailed in a shallop
All turning their heads with a truculent smile
Till a bank of green osiers
Concealed their grim faces,
Though I heard them lamenting for many a mile.

I saw three witches
Asleep in a valley,
Their heads in a row, like stones in a flood,
Till the moon, creeping upward,
Looked white through the valley,
And turned them to bushes in bright scarlet bud.

THE LITTLE CREATURE

Twinkum, twankum, twirlum and twitch—
My great-grandam—She was a Witch.
Mouse in wainscot, Saint in niche—
My great-grandam—She was a Witch;
Deadly nightshade flowers in a ditch—
My great-grandam—She was a Witch;
Long though the shroud, it grows stitch by stitch—
My great-grandam—She was a Witch;
Wean your weakling before you breech—
My great-grandam—She was a Witch;
The fattest pig's but a double flitch—
My great-grandam—She was a Witch;
Nightjars rattle, owls scritch—
My great-grandam—She was a Witch.

    Pretty and small,
    A mere nothing at all,
    Pinned up sharp in the ghost of a shawl,
    She'd straddle her down to the kirkyard wall,
    And mutter and whisper and call,
    And call. . . .

Red blood out and black blood in,
My Nannie says I'm a child of sin.
How did I choose me my witchcraft kin?
Know I as soon as dark dreams begin
Snared is my heart in a nightmare's gin;
Never from terror I out may win;
So dawn and dusk I pine, peak, thin,
Scarcely knowing t'other from which—
My great-grandam—She was a Witch.

The Golden Fleece

CHARLES KINGSLEY

The story of how Jason, in his ship Argo, *sought for the Golden Fleece is one of the most famous tales in the world. In it there is a witch-priestess, Medea, who is young and beautiful, and who helps the hero, Jason, though later she was to bring him great misery.*

The story was told originally by Greek poets, such as Pindar and Apollonius Rhodius. This version is from The Heroes *by the nineteenth-century writer, Charles Kingsley, who believed that all children should grow up knowing the great stories of Greece, whether or not they ever learned to read them in the original language.*

AND a dream came to Aietes, and filled his heart with fear. He thought he saw a shining star, which fell into his daughter's lap; and that Medea his daughter took it gladly, and carried it to the riverside, and cast it in, and there the whirling river bore it down, and out into the Euxine Sea.

Then he leapt up in fear, and bade his servants bring his chariot, that he might go down to the riverside and appease the nymphs and the heroes whose spirits haunt the bank. So he went down in his golden chariot, and his daughters by his side, Medea the fair witch-maiden, and Chalciope, who had been Phrixus' wife, and behind him a crowd of servants and soldiers, for he was a rich and mighty prince.

And as he drove down by the reedy river, he saw *Argo*

sliding up beneath the bank, and many a hero in her, like Immortals for beauty and for strength, as their weapons glittered round them in the level morning sunlight, through the white mist of the stream. But Jason was the noblest of all; for Hera, who loved him, gave him beauty and tallness and terrible manhood.

And when they came near together and looked into each other's eyes, the heroes were awed before Aietes as he shone in his chariot, like his father the glorious Sun; for his robes were of rich gold tissue, and the rays of his diadem flashed fire; and in his hand he bore a jewelled sceptre, which glittered like the stars; and sternly he looked at them under his brows, and sternly he spoke and loud: "Who are you, and what want you here, that you come to the shore of Cutaia? Do you take no account of my rule, nor of my people the Colchians who serve me, who never tired yet in the battle, and know well how to face an invader?"

And the heroes sat silent awhile before the face of that ancient king. But Hera the awful goddess put courage into Jason's heart, and he rose and shouted loudly in answer, "We are no pirates nor lawless men. We come not to plunder and to ravage, or carry away slaves from your land; but my uncle, the son of Poseidon, Pelias the Minuan king, he it is who has set me on a quest to bring home the golden fleece. And these too, my bold comrades, they are no nameless men; for some are the sons of Immortals, and some of heroes far renowned. And we too never tire in battle, and know well how to give blows and to take: yet we wish to be guests at your table: it will be better so for both."

Then Aietes' rage rushed up like a whirlwind, and his eyes flashed fire as he heard; but he crushed his anger down in his breast, and spoke mildly a cunning speech:

"If you will fight for the fleece with my Colchians, then many a man must die. But do you indeed expect to win from me the fleece in fight? So few you are that if you be worsted I can load your ship with your corpses. But if you will be ruled by me, you will find it better far to choose the best man among you, and let him fulfil the labours which I demand. Then I will give him the golden fleece for a prize and a glory to you all."

So saying, he turned his horses and drove back in silence to the town. And the Minuai sat silent with sorrow, and longed for Heracles and his strength; for there was no facing the thousands of the Colchians, and the fearful chance of war.

But Chalciope, Phrixus' widow, went weeping to the town; for she remembered her Minuan husband, and all the pleasures of her youth, while she watched the fair faces of his kinsmen, and their long locks of golden hair. And she whispered to Medea her sister, "Why should all these brave men die? why does not my father give them up the fleece, that my husband's spirit may have rest?"

And Medea's heart pitied the heroes, and Jason most of all; and she answered, "Our father is stern and terrible, and who can win the golden fleece?" But Chalciope said, "These men are not like our men; there is nothing which they cannot dare nor do."

And Medea thought of Jason and his brave countenance, and said, "If there was one among them who knew no fear, I could show him how to win the fleece."

So in the dusk of evening they went down to the river-side, Chalciope and Medea the witch-maiden, and Argus, Phrixus' son. And Argus the boy crept forward, among the beds of reeds, till he came where the heroes were sleeping, on the thwarts of the ship, beneath the bank, while

Jason kept ward on shore, and leant upon his lance full of thought. And the boy came to Jason, and said:

"I am the son of Phrixus, your cousin; and Chalciope my mother waits for you, to talk about the golden fleece."

Then Jason went boldly with the boy, and found the two princesses standing; and when Chalciope saw him she wept, and took his hands, and cried:

"O cousin of my beloved, go home before you die!"

"It would be base to go home now, fair princess, and to have sailed all these seas in vain." Then both the princesses besought him; but Jason said, "It is too late."

"But you know not," said Medea, "what he must do who would win the fleece. He must tame the two brazen-footed bulls, who breathe devouring flame; and with them he must plough ere nightfall four acres in the field of Ares; and he must sow them with serpents' teeth, of which each tooth springs up into an armed man. Then he must fight all those warriors; and little will it profit him to conquer them; for the fleece is guarded by a serpent, more huge than any mountain pine; and over his body you must step, if you would reach the golden fleece."

Then Jason laughed bitterly. "Unjustly is that fleece kept here, and by an unjust and lawless king; and unjustly shall I die in my youth, for I will attempt it ere another sun be set."

Then Medea trembled, and said, "No mortal man can reach that fleece, unless I guide him through. For round it, beyond the river, is a wall full nine ells high, with lofty towers and buttresses, and mighty gates of threefold brass; and over the gates the wall is arched, with golden battlements above. And over the gateway sits Brimo, the wild witch-huntress of the woods, brandishing a pine-torch in her hands, while her mad hounds howl around. No man dare meet her or look on her, but only I her priestess, and she watches far and wide lest any stranger should come near."

"No wall so high but it may be climbed at last, and no wood so thick but it may be crawled through; no serpent so wary but he may be charmed, or witch-queen so fierce but spells may soothe her; and I may yet win the golden fleece, if a wise maiden help bold men."

And he looked at Medea cunningly, and held her with his glittering eye, till she blushed and trembled, and said:

"Who can face the fire of the bulls' breath, and fight ten thousand armed men?"

"He whom you help," said Jason, flattering her, "for your fame is spread over all the earth. Are you not the queen of all enchantresses, wiser even than your sister Circe, in her fairy island in the West?"

"Would that I were with my sister Circe in her fairy island in the West, far away from sore temptation and thoughts which tear the heart! But if it must be so—for why should you die?—I have an ointment here; I made it from the magic ice-flower which sprang from Prometheus' wound, above the clouds on Caucasus, in the dreary fields of snow. Anoint yourself with that, and you shall have in you seven men's strength—and anoint your shield with it, and neither fire nor sword can harm you. But what you begin you must end before sunset, for its virtue lasts only one day. And anoint your helmet with it before you sow the serpents' teeth; and when the sons of earth spring up, cast your helmet among their ranks, and the deadly crop of the War-gods' field will mow itself, and perish."

Then Jason fell on his knees before her, and thanked her and kissed her hands; and she gave him the vase of ointment, and fled trembling through the reeds. And Jason told his comrades what had happened, and showed them the box of ointment; and all rejoiced but Idas, and he grew mad with envy.

And at sunrise Jason went and bathed, and anointed himself from head to foot, and his shield, and his helmet, and his weapons, and bade his comrades try the spell. So they tried to bend his lance, but it stood like an iron bar; and Idas in spite hewed at it with his sword, but the blade flew to splinters in his face. Then they hurled their lances at his shield, but the spear-points turned like lead; and Coeneus tried to throw him, but he never stirred a foot; and Polydeuces struck him with his fist a blow which would have killed an ox; but Jason only smiled, and the heroes danced about him with delight; and he leapt, and ran, and shouted, in the joy of that enormous strength, till the sun rose, and it was time to go and to claim Aietes' promise.

So he sent up Telamon and Aithalides to tell Aietes that he was ready for the fight; and they went up among the marble walls, and beneath the roofs of gold, and stood in Aietes' hall, while he grew pale with rage.

"Fulfil your promise to us, child of the blazing Sun. Give us the serpents' teeth, and let loose the fiery bulls; for we have found a champion among us who can win the golden fleece."

And Aietes bit his lips, for he fancied that they had fled away by night: but he could not go back from his promise; so he gave them the serpents' teeth.

Then he called for his chariot and his horses, and sent heralds through all the town; and all the people went out with him to the dreadful War-god's field.

And there Aietes sat upon his throne, with his warriors on each hand, thousands and tens of thousands, clothed from head to foot in steel chain-mail. And the people and the women crowded to every window, and bank, and wall; while the Minuai stood together, a mere handful in the midst of that great host.

And Chalciope was there and Argus, trembling, and Medea, wrapped closely in her veil; but Aietes did not know that she was muttering cunning spells between her lips.

Then Jason cried, "Fulfil your promise, and let your fiery bulls come forth."

Then Aietes bade open the gates, and the magic bulls leapt out. Their brazen hoofs rang upon the ground, and their nostrils sent out sheets of flame, as they rushed with lowered heads upon Jason; but he never flinched a step. The flame of their breath swept round him, but it singed not a hair of his head; and the bulls stopped short and trembled when Medea began her spell.

Then Jason sprang upon the nearest, and seized him by the horn; and up and down they wrestled, till the bull fell grovelling on his knees; for the heart of the brute died within him, and his mighty limbs were loosed, beneath the steadfast eye of that dark witch-maiden, and the magic whisper of her lips.

So both the bulls were tamed and yoked; and Jason bound them to the plough, and goaded them onward with his lance, till he had ploughed the sacred field.

And all the Minuai shouted; but Aietes bit his lips with rage; for the half of Jason's work was over, and the sun was yet high in heaven.

Then he took the serpents' teeth and sowed them, and waited what would befall. But Medea looked at him and at his helmet, lest he should forget the lesson she had taught.

And every furrow heaved and bubbled, and out of every

clod arose a man. Out of the earth they rose by thousands, each clad from head to foot in steel, and drew their swords and rushed on Jason, where he stood in the midst alone.

Then the Minuai grew pale with fear for him; but Aietes laughed a bitter laugh. "See! If I had not warriors enough already round me, I could call them out from the bosom of the earth."

But Jason snatched off his helmet, and hurled it into the thickest of the throng. And blind madness came upon them, suspicion, hate and fear; and one cried to his fellow, "Thou didst strike me!" and another, "Thou art Jason; thou shalt die!" So fury seized those earth-born phantoms, and each turned his hand against the rest; and they fought and were never weary, till they all lay dead upon the ground. Then the magic furrows opened, and the kind earth took them home into her breast; and the grass grew up all green again above them, and Jason's work was done.

Then the Minuai rose and shouted, till Prometheus heard them from his crag. And Jason cried, "Lead me to the fleece this moment, before the sun goes down."

But Aietes thought—"He has conquered the bulls; and sown and reaped the deadly crop. Who is this who is proof against all magic? He may kill the serpent yet." So he delayed, and sat taking counsel with his princes till the sun went down and all was dark. Then he bade a herald cry, "Every man to his home for tonight. Tomorrow we will meet these heroes, and speak about the golden fleece."

Then he turned and looked at Medea: "This is your doing, false witch-maid! You have helped these yellow-haired strangers, and brought shame upon your father and yourself!" Medea shrank and trembled, and her face grew pale with fear; and Aietes knew that she was guilty, and whispered, "If they win the fleece you die!"

But the Minuai marched toward their ship, growling like lions cheated of their prey; for they saw that Aietes meant to mock them, and to cheat them out of all their toil. And Oileus said, "Let us go to the grove together, and take the fleece by force."

And Idas the rash cried, "Let us draw lots who shall go in first; for, while the dragon is devouring one, the rest can slay him and carry off the fleece in peace." But Jason held them back, though he praised them; for he hoped for Medea's help.

And after a while Medea came trembling, and wept a long while before she spoke. And at last—

"My end is come, and I must die; for my father has found out that I have helped you. You he would kill if he dared; but he will not harm you, because you have been his guests. Go then, go, and remember poor Medea when you are far away across the sea." But all the heroes cried:

"If you die, we die with you; for without you we cannot win the fleece, and home we will not go without it, but fall here fighting to the last man."

"You need not die," said Jason. "Flee home with us across the sea. Show us first how to win the fleece; for you can do it. Why else are you priestess of the grove? Show us but how to win the fleece, and come with us, and you shall be my queen, and rule over the rich princes of the Minuai, in Iolcos by the sea."

And all the heroes pressed round, and vowed to her that she should be their queen.

Medea wept, and shuddered, and hid her face in her hands; for her heart yearned after her sisters and her play-fellows, and the home where she was brought up as a child. But at last she looked up at Jason, and spoke between her sobs:

"Must I leave my home and my people, to wander with strangers across the sea? The lot is cast, and I must endure it. I will show you how to win the golden fleece. Bring up your ship to the wood-side, and moor her there against the bank; and let Jason come up at midnight, and one brave comrade with him, and meet me beneath the wall."

Then all the heroes cried together—"I will go!" "and I!" And Idas the rash grew mad with envy; for he longed to be foremost in all things. But Medea calmed them, and said, "Orpheus shall go with Jason, and bring his magic harp; for I hear of him that he is the king of all minstrels, and can charm all things on earth."

And Orpheus laughed for joy, and clapped his hands, because the choice had fallen on him; for in those days poets and singers were as bold warriors as the best.

So at midnight they went up the bank, and found Medea; and beside came Absyrtus her young brother, leading a yearling lamb. Then Medea brought them to a thicket beside the War-god's gate; and there she bade Jason dig a ditch, and kill the lamb, and leave it there, and strew on it magic herbs and honey from the honeycomb.

Then sprang up through the earth, with the red fire flashing before her, Brimo the wild witch-huntress, while her mad hounds howled around. She had one head like a horse's, and another like a ravening hound's, and another like a hissing snake's, and a sword in either hand. And she leapt into the ditch with her hounds, and they ate and drank their fill, while Jason and Orpheus trembled, and Medea hid her eyes. And at last the witch-queen vanished, and fled with her hounds into the woods; and the bars of the gates fell down, and the brazen doors flew wide, and Medea and the heroes ran forward and hurried through the poison wood, among the dark stems of the mighty beeches, guided by the gleam of the golden fleece, until they saw it hanging on one vast tree in the midst. And Jason would have sprung to seize it; but Medea held him back, and pointed, shuddering, to the tree-foot, where the mighty serpent lay, coiled in and out among the roots, with a body like a mountain pine. His coils stretched many a fathom, spangled with bronze and gold; and half of him they could see, but no more, for the rest lay in the darkness far beyond.

And when he saw them coming he lifted up his head, and watched them with his small bright eyes, and flashed his forked tongue, and roared like the fire among the woodlands, till the forest tossed and groaned. For his cries shook the trees from leaf to root, and swept over the long reaches of the river, and over Aietes' hall, and woke the sleepers in the city, till mothers clasped their children in their fear.

But Medea called gently to him, and he stretched out his long spotted neck, and licked her hand, and looked up in her face, as if to ask for food. Then she made a sign to Orpheus, and he began his magic song.

And as he sang, the forest grew calm again, and the leaves on every tree hung still; and the serpent's head sank down, and his brazen coils grew limp, and his glittering eyes closed lazily, till he breathed as gently as a child, while Orpheus called to pleasant Slumber, who gives peace to men, and beasts, and waves.

Then Jason leapt forward warily, and stepped across that mighty snake, and tore the fleece from off the tree-trunk; and the four rushed down the garden, to the bank where the *Argo* lay.

There was a silence for a moment, while Jason held the golden fleece on high. Then he cried—"Go now, good *Argo*, swift and steady, if ever you would see Pelion more."

And she went, as the heroes drove her, grim and silent all, with muffled oars, till the pine-wood bent like willow in their hands, and stout *Argo* groaned beneath their strokes.

On and on, beneath the dewy darkness, they fled swiftly down the swirling stream; underneath black walls, and temples, and the castles of the princes of the East; past sluice-mouths, and fragrant gardens, and groves of all strange fruits; past marshes where fat kine lay sleeping, and long beds of whispering reeds; till they heard the merry music of the surge upon the bar, as it tumbled in the moonlight all alone.

Into the surge they rushed, and *Argo* leapt the breakers like a horse; for she knew the time was come to show her mettle, and win honour for the heroes and herself.

Into the surge they rushed, and *Argo* leapt the breakers like a horse, till the heroes stopped all panting, each man upon his oar, as she slid into the still broad sea.

Then Orpheus took his harp and sang a pæan, till the heroes' hearts rose high again; and they rowed on stoutly and steadfastly, away into the darkness of the West.

Foretelling the Future

Was a witch really connected with the first discoverers of America? Yes, according to The Saga of Eric the Red.

This saga tells how Eric's son Leif—Leif Ericsson as he is known—found the shores of North America in about the year 1000. This was some five hundred years earlier than Columbus. He named the country Vinland. The ancient tradition that Norse adventurers sailed right across the Atlantic is found also in Icelandic annals. It could very well have been possible, as at that time the climate around Iceland and Greenland was relatively mild, so there was less ice on the seas than there was later. Recently, there has been a fascinating confirmation of the saga. A map has been discovered which was probably produced just before Columbus was born. It shows a country called Vinlanda across the Atlantic. Any doubts you may have about the witch's power to foretell the future need not affect the essential part of the story.

This story of the meeting point of Christian and pagan belief is told by Andrew Lang. He was a Scottish scholar and story-teller born in 1844. Many thousands of people since have had their first acquaintance with the great stories of the past through his books, which range from collections of fairy-tales to translations of Homer. The book from which this story is taken is called, appropriately, The True Story Book.

The prophecies which follow are the famous ones which the three witches gave to Macbeth. They set him on a path of murder, in order to seize and to hold the Scottish throne. The prophecies are given here in two forms: first from Holinshed's Chronicles, *or* Histories, *which Shakespeare used as a source for many of his plays: and secondly, in a scene from Shakespeare's* Macbeth. *Shakespeare is much more concerned than Holinshed to show the strangeness of the witches and the violence of Macbeth's reaction to them.*

THE SPELL-SONG

ANDREW LANG

Hundreds of years before Columbus discovered America, there lived in Iceland a man named Eric the Red. His father had slain a man in Norway and fled with his family to Iceland. Eric, too, was a dangerous man. His servants did mischief on the farm of a neighbour, who slew them. Then Eric slew the farmer and also Holmgang Hrafn, a famous duellist, of whom the country was well rid. Eric was banished from that place, and, in his new home, had a new quarrel. He lent some furniture to a man who refused to restore it. Eric, therefore, carried off his goods, and the other pursued him. They fought, and Eric killed him. For this he was made an outlaw, and went sailing to discover new countries. He found one, where he settled, calling it Greenland, because, he said, people would come there more readily if it had a good name.

One Thorbiorn, among others, sailed to Greenland, but came in an unlucky time, for fish were scarce, and some settlers were drowned. At that day, some of the newcomers were Christians, some still worshipped the old gods, Thor and Woden, and practised magic. These sent for a prophetess to tell them what the end of their new colony would be. It is curious to know what a real witch was like, and how she behaved, so we shall copy the story from the old Icelandic book.

When she came in the evening, with the man who had been sent to meet her, she was clad in a dark-blue cloak, fastened with a strap and set with stones quite down to the hem. She wore glass beads around her neck, and upon her head a black lambskin hood, lined with white catskin. In her hands she carried a staff, upon which there was a knob,

which was ornamented with brass, and set up with stones
about the knob. Circling her waist she wore a girdle of
touchwood, and attached to it a great skin pouch, in which
she kept the charms she used when she was practising her
sorcery. She wore upon her feet shaggy calfskin shoes,
with long tough lachets, upon the end of which there were
large brass buttons. She had catskin gloves upon her hands;
the gloves were white inside and lined with fur. When she
entered, all of the folk felt it to be their duty to offer her
becoming greetings. She received the salutations of each
individual according as he pleased her.

Yeoman Thorkel took the sibyl by the hand, and led
her to the seat which had been made ready for her.
Thorkel made her run her eyes over man and beast and
home. She had little to say concerning all these. The tables
were brought forth in the evening, and it remains to be
told what manner of food was prepared for the prophetess.
A porridge of goat's beestings was made for her, and for
meat there were dressed the hearts of every kind of beast
that could be obtained there. She had a brass spoon, and a
knife with a handle of walrus tusk, with a double hasp of
brass around the haft, and from this the point was broken.
And when the tables were removed, Yeoman Thorkel
approaches the prophetess Thorbiorg, and asks how she is
pleased with the home, and the character of the folk, and
how speedily she would be likely to become aware of that
concerning which he had questioned her, and which the
people were anxious to know. She replied that she could
not give an opinion in this matter before the morrow,
after that she had slept there through the night.

And on the morrow, when the day was far spent, such
preparations were made as were necessary to enable her to
accomplish her soothsaying. She bade them bring her those

women who knew the incantation which she required to work her spells, and which she called Warlocks; but such women were not to be found. Thereupon a search was made throughout the house, to see whether anyone knew this incantation.

Then said Gudrid, Thorbiorn's daughter: "Although I am neither skilled in the black art nor a sibyl, yet my foster-mother, Halldis, taught me in Iceland that spell-song which she called Warlocks."

Thorbiorg answered: "Then thou art wise in season!"

Gudrid replied: "This is an incantation and ceremony of such a kind that I do not mean to lend it any aid, for I am a Christian woman."

Thorbiorg answered: "It might so be that thou couldst give thy help to the company here, and still be no worse woman than before; however, I leave it with Thorkel to provide for my needs."

Thorkel now so urged Gudrid that she said she must needs comply with his wishes. The women then made a ring round about, while Thorbiorg sat up on the spell-dais. Gudrid then sang the song, so sweet and well, that no one remembered ever before to have heard the melody sung with so fair a voice as this.

The sorceress thanked her for the song and said: "She has indeed lured many spirits hither, who think it pleasant to hear this song, those who were wont to forsake us hitherto and refuse to submit themselves to us. Many things are now revealed to me, which hitherto have been hidden, both from me and from others. And I am able to announce that this period of famine will not endure longer, but the season will mend as spring approaches. The visitation of disease, which has been so long upon you, will disappear sooner than expected."

After this, Thorbiorn sailed to the part of Greenland where Eric the Red lived, and there was received with open arms. Eric had two sons, one called Thorstein, the other Leif, and it was Leif who afterwards discovered Vineland the Good, that is the coast of America, somewhere between Nova Scotia and New England. He found it by accident. He had been in Norway at the court of king Olaf, who bade him proclaim Christianity in Greenland. As he was sailing thither, Leif was driven by tempests out of his course, and came across coasts which he had never heard of, where wild vines grew, and hence he called that shore Vineland the Good. The vine did not grow, of course, in Iceland. But Leif had with him a German, Tyrker, and one day, when they were on shore, Tyrker was late in joining the rest. He was very much excited and spoke in the German tongue, saying "I have found something new, vines and grapes." Then they filled their boat full of grapes, and sailed away. He also brought away some men from a wreck, and with these, and the message of the Gospel, he sailed back to Greenland, to his father, Eric the Red, and from that day he was named Leif the Lucky. But Eric had no great mind to become a Christian: he had been born to believe in Thor and his own sword.

THE WEIRD SISTERS (I)

RAPHAEL HOLINSHED

Here is an account of Macbeth in the words that Shakespeare himself must have read before he wrote the most famous of all plays involving witches. It comes from "The Chronicles of England and Ireland" by Raphael Holinshed.[1]

IT fortuned as Macbeth and Banquo journeyed towards Forres, where the King then lay, they went sporting by the way together without any other company, save only themselves, passing through the woods and fields, when suddenly in the middle of a land, there met them three women in strange and ferly apparel, resembling creatures of an elder world, whom they attentively beheld, wondering much at the sight. The first of them spake and said: "All hail, Macbeth, Thane of Glamis," (for he had lately entered into that dignity and office by the death of his father, Sinel). The second of them said: "Hail, Macbeth, Thane of Cawdor." But the third said: "All hail, Macbeth, that hereafter shall be King of Scotland."

Then Banquo: "What manner of women," saith he, "are you that seem so little favourable unto me, whereas to my fellow here, beside high office, you assign also the kingdom, appointing forth nothing for me at all?"

"Yes," saith the first of them, "we promise greater benefits unto thee than unto him, for he shall reign in deed, but with an unlucky end: neither shall he leave any issue behind him to succeed in his place. Contrarily, thou in

[1] Published in 1577, it was an important source for a number of Shakespeare's plays.

deed shall not reign at all, but of thee those shall be born which shall govern the Scottish kingdom by long order of continual descent." Herewith the foresaid women vanished immediately out of their sight.

This was reputed at the first but some vain fantastical illusion by Macbeth and Banquo, in so much that Banquo would call Macbeth in jest, "King of Scotland", and Macbeth again would call him in sport likewise, "the father of many kings". But afterwards the common opinion was, that these women were either the weird sisters, that is (as you would say) the goddesses of destiny, or else some nymphs or fairies, endued with knowledge of prophecy by their necromantic science, because everything came to pass as they had spoken.

THE WEIRD SISTERS (2)

WILLIAM SHAKESPEARE

Here, to show how prose can be turned into poetry, is Shakespeare's account of the same meeting in his play, "Macbeth".

A heath. Enter Macbeth and Banquo.
Macbeth: So foul and fair a day I have not seen.
Banquo: How far is't called to Forres?—What are these
  So wither'd and so wild in their attire,
  That look not like th' inhabitants of the earth,
  But yet are on't?—Live you? or are you aught
  That man may question? You seem to understand me,
  By each at once her choppy finger laying
  Upon her skinny lips:—you should be women,

And yet your beards forbid me to interpret
That you are so.
Macbeth: Speak, if you can:—what are you?
First Witch: All hail, Macbeth! hail to thee, thane of
Glamis!
Second Witch: All hail, Macbeth! hail to thee, thane of
Cawdor!
Third Witch: All hail, Macbeth, that shalt be king hereafter!
Banquo: Good sir, why do you start and seem to fear
Things that do sound so fair?—I' th' name of truth
Are ye fantastical, or that indeed
Which outwardly ye show? My noble partner
You greet with present grace, and great prediction
Of noble having and of royal hope,
That he seems rapt withal: to me you speak not:
If you can look into the seeds of time,
And say which grain will grow and which will not,
Speak, then, to me, who neither beg nor fear
Your favours nor your hate.
First Witch: Hail!
Second Witch: Hail!
Third Witch: Hail!
First Witch: Lesser than Macbeth, and greater.
Second Witch: Not so happy, yet much happier.
Third Witch: Thou shalt get kings, though thou be none:
Banquo: So, all hail, Macbeth and Banquo!
First Witch: Banquo and Macbeth, all hail!
Macbeth: Stay, you imperfect speakers, tell me more:
By Sinel's death I know I am thane of Glamis;
But how of Cawdor? the thane of Cawdor lives,
A prosperous gentleman; and to be king
Stands not within the prospect of belief,
No more than to be Cawdor. Say from whence

You owe this strange intelligence? or why
Upon this blasted heath you stop our way
With such prophetic greeting? Speak, I charge you.
   Witches vanish.
Banquo: The earth hath bubbles, as the water has,
   And these are of them:—wither are they vanish'd?
Macbeth: Into the air: and what seemed corporal melted
   As breath into the wind. Would they had stayed!

(As Holinshed says, the prophecies came true. Immediately afterwards, Macbeth heard that he had been made thane of Cawdor, the previous thane having lost his title because of his treason. Later, Macbeth became king, by murdering Duncan. It was left to the witches themselves to show him how the last part of their prophecies would come true, when they called up a long line of Banquo's descendants, all of them crowned kings.)

Baba Yaga and the Little Girl with the Kind Heart

ARTHUR RANSOME

Baba Yaga is the traditional witch of Russian folk-lore. This story about her is re-told by Arthur Ransome in Old Peter's Russian Tales. *It shows how the malice and cruelty of witchcraft is overcome by a little magic, and, more important, by kindness.*

ONCE upon a time there was a widowed old man who lived alone in a hut with his little daughter. Very merry they were together, and they used to smile at each other over a table just piled with bread and jam. Everything went well, until the old man took it into his head to marry again.

Yes, the old man became foolish in the years of his old age, and he took another wife. And so the poor little girl had a stepmother. And after that everything changed. There was no more bread and jam on the table, and no more playing bo-peep, first this side of the samovar and then that, as she sat with her father at tea. It was worse than that, for she never did sit at tea. The stepmother said that everything that went wrong was the little girl's fault. And the old man believed his new wife, and so there were no more kind words for his little daughter. Day after day the stepmother used to say that the little girl was too naughty to sit at table. And then she would throw her a crust, and tell her to get out of the hut, and go and eat it somewhere else.

And the poor little girl used to go away by herself into the shed in the yard, and wet the dry crust with her tears, and eat it all alone. Ah me! she often wept for the old days, and she often wept at the thought of the days that were to come.

Mostly she wept because she was all alone, until one day she found a little friend in the shed. She was hunched up in a corner of the shed, eating her crust and crying bitterly, when she heard a little noise. It was like this. Scratch. Scratch. It was just that, a little grey mouse who lived in a hole.

Out he came, his little pointed nose and his long whiskers, his little round ears and his bright eyes. Out came his little humpy body and his long tail. And then he sat up on his hind-legs, and curled his tail twice round himself and looked at the little girl.

The little girl, who had a kind heart, forgot all her sorrows, and took a scrap of her crust and threw it to the little mouse. The mouseykin nibbled and nibbled, and there, it was gone, and he was looking for another. She gave him another bit, and presently that was gone, and another and another, until there was no crust left for the little girl. Well, she didn't mind that. You see, she was so happy seeing the little mouse nibbling and nibbling.

When the crust was done the mouseykin looks up at her with his little bright eyes, and "Thank you," he says, in a little squeaky voice. "Thank you," he says; "you are a kind little girl, and I am only a mouse, and I've eaten all your crust. But there is one thing I can do for you, and that is to tell you to take care. The old woman in the hut (and that was the cruel stepmother) is own sister to Baba Yaga, the bony-legged, the witch. So if ever she sends you on a message to your aunt, you come and tell me. For Baba Yaga would eat you soon enough with her iron teeth if you did not know what to do."

"Oh, thank you," said the little girl; and just then she heard the stepmother calling to her to come in and clean up the tea things, and tidy the house, and brush out the floor, and clean everybody's boots.

So off she had to go.

When she went in she had a good look at her stepmother, and sure enough she had a long nose, and she was as bony as a fish with all the flesh picked off, and the little girl thought of Baba Yaga and shivered, though she did not feel so bad when she remembered the mouseykin out there in the shed in the yard.

The very next morning it happened. The old man went off to pay a visit to some friends of his in the next village. And as soon as the old man was out of sight the wicked stepmother called the little girl.

"You are to go today to your dear little aunt in the forest," says she, "and ask her for a needle and thread to mend a shirt."

"But here is a needle and thread," said the little girl.

"Hold your tongue," says the stepmother, and she gnashes her teeth, and they make a noise like clattering tongs. "Hold your tongue," she says. "Didn't I tell you you are to go today to your dear little aunt to ask for a needle and thread to mend a shirt?"

"How shall I find her?" says the little girl, nearly ready to cry, for she knew that her aunt was Baba Yaga, the bony-legged, the witch.

The stepmother took hold of the little girl's nose and pinched it.

"That is your nose," she says. "Can you feel it?"

"Yes," says the poor little girl.

"You must go along the road into the forest till you come to a fallen tree; then you must turn to your left, and then follow your nose and you will find her," says the stepmother. "Now, be off with you, lazy one. Here is some food for you to eat by the way." She gave the little girl a bundle wrapped up in a towel.

The little girl wanted to go into the shed to tell the mouseykin she was going to Baba Yaga, and to ask what she should do. But she looked back, and there was the stepmother at the door watching her. So she had to go straight on.

She walked along the road through the forest till she came to the fallen tree. Then she turned to the left. Her nose was still hurting where the stepmother had pinched it, so she knew she had to go straight ahead. She was just setting out when she heard a little noise under the fallen tree.

"Scratch. Scratch."

And out jumped the little mouse, and sat up in the road in front of her.

"O mouseykin, mouseykin," says the little girl, "my stepmother has sent me to her sister. And that is Baba Yaga, the bony-legged, the witch, and I do not know what to do."

"It will not be difficult," says the little mouse, "because of your kind heart. Take all the things you find in the road, and do with them what you like. Then you will escape from Baba Yaga, and everything will be well."

"Are you hungry, mouseykin?" said the little girl.

"I could nibble, I think," says the little mouse.

The little girl unfastened the towel, and there was nothing

in it but stones. That was what the stepmother had given the little girl to eat by the way.

"Oh, I'm so sorry," says the little girl. "There's nothing for you to eat."

"Isn't there?" said mouseykin, and as she looked at them the little girl saw the stones turn to bread and jam. The little girl sat down on the fallen tree, and the little mouse sat beside her, and they ate bread and jam until they were not hungry any more.

"Keep the towel," says the little mouse; "I think it will be useful. And remember what I said about the things you find on the way. And now good-bye," says he.

"Good-bye," says the little girl, and runs along.

As she was running along she found a nice new handkerchief lying in the road. She picked it up and took it with her. Then she found a little bottle of oil. She picked it up and took it with her. Then she found some scraps of meat.

"Perhaps I'd better take them too," she said; and she took them.

Then she found a gay blue ribbon, and she took that. Then she found a little loaf of good bread, and she took that too.

"I dare say somebody will like it," she said.

And then she came to the hut of Baba Yaga, the bony-legged, the witch. There was a high fence round it with big gates. When she pushed them open they squeaked miserably, as if it hurt them to move. The little girl was sorry for them.

"How lucky," she says, "that I picked up the bottle of oil." And she poured the oil into the hinges of the gates.

Inside the railing was Baba Yaga's hut, and it stood on hen's legs and walked about the yard. And in the yard there was standing Baba Yaga's servant, and she was crying bitterly because of the tasks Baba Yaga set her to do. She was crying bitterly and wiping her eyes on her petticoat.

"How lucky," says the little girl, "that I picked up a handkerchief." And she gave the handkerchief to Baba Yaga's servant, who wiped her eyes on it and smiled through her tears.

Close by the hut was a huge dog, very thin, gnawing a dry crust.

"How lucky," says the little girl, "that I picked up a loaf." And she gave the loaf to the dog, and he gobbled it up and licked his lips.

The little girl went bravely up to the hut and knocked on the door.

"Come in," says Baba Yaga.

The little girl went in, and there was Baba Yaga, the bony-legged, the witch, sitting weaving at a loom. In a corner of the hut was a thin black cat watching a mousehole.

"Good day to you, auntie," says the little girl, trying not to tremble.

"Good day to you, niece," says Baba Yaga.

"My stepmother has sent me to you to ask for a needle and thread to mend a shirt."

"Very well," says Baba Yaga, smiling, and showing her iron teeth. "You sit down here at the loom, and go on with my weaving, while I go and get you the needle and thread."

The little girl sat down at the loom and began to weave.

Baba Yaga went out and called to her servant, "Go, make the bath hot, and scrub my niece. Scrub her clean. I'll make a dainty meal of her."

The servant came in for the jug. The little girl begged her, "Be not too quick in making the fire, and carry the water in a sieve." The servant smiled but said nothing, because she was afraid of Baba Yaga. But she took a very long time about getting the bath ready.

Baba Yaga came to the window and asked:

"Are you weaving, little niece? Are you weaving, my pretty?"

"I am weaving, auntie," says the little girl.

When Baba Yaga went away from the window, the little girl spoke to the thin black cat who was watching the mouse-hole.

"What are you doing, thin black cat?"

"Watching for a mouse," says the thin black cat. "I haven't had any dinner for three days."

"How lucky," says the little girl, "that I picked up the scraps of meat." And she gave them to the thin black cat. The thin black cat gobbled them up, and said to the little girl:

"Little girl, do you want to get out of this?"

"Catkin dear," says the little girl, "I do want to get out of this, for Baba Yaga is going to eat me with her iron teeth."

"Well," says the cat, "I will help you."

Just then Baba Yaga came to the window.

"Are you weaving, little niece?" she asked. "Are you weaving, my pretty?"

"I am weaving, auntie," says the little girl, working away, while the loom went clickety clack, clickety clack.

Baba Yaga went away.

Says the thin black cat to the little girl: "You have a comb in your hair, and you have a towel. Take them and run for it, while Baba Yaga is in the bath-house. When Baba Yaga chases after you, you must listen; and when she is close to you throw away the towel, and it will turn into a big, wide river. It will take her a little time to get over that. But when she does, you must listen; and as soon as she is close to you throw away the comb, and it will sprout up into such a forest that she will never get through it at all."

"But she'll hear the loom stop," says the little girl.

"I'll see to that," says the thin black cat.

The cat took the little girl's place at the loom.

Clickety clack, clickety clack; the loom never stopped for a moment.

The little girl looked to see that Baba Yaga was in the bath-house, and then she jumped down from the little hut on hen's legs, and ran to the gates as fast as her legs could flicker.

The big dog leapt up to tear her to pieces. Just as he was going to spring on her he saw who she was.

"Why, this is the little girl who gave me the loaf," says he. "A good journey to you, little girl;" and he lay down again with his head between his paws.

When she came to the gates they opened quietly, quietly, without making any noise at all, because of the oil she had poured into their hinges.

Outside the gates there was a little birch tree that beat her in the eyes so that she could not go by.

"How lucky," says the little girl, "that I picked up the ribbon." And she tied up the birch tree with the pretty blue ribbon. And the birch tree was so pleased with the ribbon that it stood still, admiring itself, and let the little girl go by.

How she did run!

Meanwhile the thin black cat sat at the loom. Clickety clack, clickety clack, sang the loom; but you never saw such a tangle as the tangle made by the thin black cat.

And presently Baba Yaga came to the window.

"Are you weaving, little niece?" she asked. "Are you weaving, my pretty?"

"I am weaving, auntie," says the thin black cat, tangling and tangling, while the loom went clickety clack, clickety clack.

"That's not the voice of my little dinner," says Baba Yaga, and she jumped into the hut, gnashing her iron teeth; and there was no little girl, but only the thin black cat, sitting at the loom, tangling and tangling the threads.

"Grr," says Baba Yaga, and jumps for the cat, and begins banging it about. "Why didn't you tear the little girl's eyes out?"

"In all the years I have served you," says the cat, "you have only given me one little bone; but the kind little girl gave me scraps of meat."

Baba Yaga threw the cat into a corner, and went out into the yard.

"Why didn't you squeak when she opened you?" she asked the gates.

"Why didn't you tear her to pieces?" she asked the dog.

"Why didn't you beat her in the face, and not let her go by?" she asked the birch tree.

"Why were you so long in getting the bath ready? If you had been quicker, she never would have got away," said Baba Yaga to the servant.

And she rushed about the yard, beating them all, and scolding at the top of her voice.

"Ah!" said the gates, "in all the years we have served you, you never eased us with water; but the kind little girl poured good oil into our hinges."

"Ah!" said the dog, "in all the years I've served you, you never threw me anything but burnt crusts; but the kind little girl gave me a good loaf."

"Ah!" said the little birch tree, "in all the years I've served you, you never tied me up, even with thread; but the kind little girl tied me up with a gay blue ribbon."

"Ah!" said the servant, "in all the years I've served you, you have never given me even a rag; but the kind little girl gave me a pretty handkerchief."

Baba Yaga gnashed at them with her iron teeth. Then she jumped into the mortar and sat down. She drove it along with the pestle, and swept up her tracks with a besom, and flew off in pursuit of the little girl.

The little girl ran and ran. She put her ear to the ground and listened. Bang, bang, bangety bang! She could hear Baba Yaga beating the mortar with the pestle. Baba Yaga was quite close. There she was, beating with the pestle and sweeping with the besom, coming along the road.

As quickly as she could, the little girl took out the towel and threw it on the ground. And the towel grew bigger and bigger, and wetter and wetter, and there was a deep, broad river between Baba Yaga and the little girl.

The little girl turned and ran on. How she ran!

Baba Yaga came flying up in the mortar. But the mortar could not float in the river with Baba Yaga inside. She drove it in, but only got wet for her trouble. Tongs and pokers tumbling down a chimney are nothing to the noise she made as she gnashed her iron teeth. She turned home, and went flying back to the little hut on hen's legs. Then she got together all her cattle, and drove them to the river.

"Drink, drink!" she screamed at them; and the cattle drank up all the river to the last drop. And Baba Yaga, sitting in the mortar, drove it with the pestle, and swept up her tracks with the besom, and flew over the dry bed of the river and on in pursuit of the little girl.

The little girl put her ear to the ground and listened.

Bang, bang, bangety bang! She could hear Baba Yaga beating the mortar with the pestle. Nearer and nearer came the noise, and there was Baba Yaga, beating with the pestle and sweeping with the besom, coming along the road close behind.

The little girl threw down the comb, and it grew bigger and bigger, and its teeth sprouted up into a thick forest, thicker than this forest where we live—so thick that not even Baba Yaga could force her way through. And Baba Yaga, gnashing her teeth and screaming with rage and disappointment, turned round and drove away home to her little hut on hen's legs.

The little girl ran on home. She was afraid to go in and see her stepmother, so she ran into the shed.

Scratch, scratch! Out came the little mouse.

"So you got away all right, my dear," says the little mouse. "Now run in. Don't be afraid. Your father is back, and you must tell him all about it."

The little girl went into the house.

"Where have you been?" says her father, "and why are you so out of breath?"

The stepmother turned yellow when she saw her, and her eyes glowed, and her teeth ground together until they broke.

But the little girl was not afraid, and she went to her father and climbed on his knee, and told him everything just as it had happened. And when the old man knew that the stepmother had sent his little daughter to be eaten by Baba Yaga, he was so angry that he drove her out of the hut, and ever afterwards lived alone with the little girl. Much better it was for both of them.

And the little mouse came and lived in the hut, and every day it used to sit up on the table and eat crumbs, and warm its paws on the little girl's glass of tea.

Witch Flights

One of the most common beliefs about witches is the idea that they can fly. Here are three variations upon that theme. The first comes from a play, The Witch, by Thomas Middleton, who was born a few years after Shakespeare. The second is from The Midnight Folk by John Masefield, who is Poet Laureate at the present time. The third story is a mixture of old and new. It comes from a modern book, Folktales of Norway by Reidar Thorwald Christiansen, translated by Pat Shaw Iversen. The actual story is old; it is one of the tales that country people used to tell round the hearth during the long nights of the northern winter.

One feature of the last story has a basis in fact. There do survive recipes for "flying ointments". Women who claimed to be witches rubbed these not on to a broomstick or anything else, but into their own bodies. The ointments included various grisly ingredients, and also plants such as aconite which is a poison affecting the heart-beats. It is possible that the aconite was absorbed through cuts and sores on the body, and caused feelings of dizziness which were mistaken for flying.

A WITCH'S SONG

THOMAS MIDDLETON

Now I'm furnished for the flight,
Now I go, now I fly,
Malkin my sweet spirit and I.
O, what a dainty pleasure 'tis
To ride in the air
When the moon shines fair,
And sing and dance and toy and kiss.
Over woods, high rocks and mountains,
Over seas, our mistress' fountains,
Over steeples, towers, and turrets,
We fly by night, 'mongst troops of spirits.

No ring of bells to our ears sounds,
No howls of wolves, no yelp of hounds.
No, not the noise of water's breach,
Or cannon's throat can our height reach.

THE BOY ON A BROOMSTICK

JOHN MASEFIELD

Nibbins the cat takes Kay to see the strange things that happen at night in the large, lonely country house where he lives. Kay finds some strange inhabitants, and rides on "the horse that is hayless".

While Kay was watching, Nibbins put a paw on his arm.

"Don't speak," he said. "Mrs Pouncer is going to sing. Come along quietly. You'll enjoy this."

He led Kay along a narrow corridor to another passage, where there were more eyelet holes. Kay looked through the eyes of Great-grandmamma Siskin's portrait into the dining-room; but what did he see?

There were seven old witches in tall black hats and long scarlet cloaks sitting round the table for a very good supper: the cold goose and chine which had been hot at middle-day dinner, and the plum cake which was new for tea.

They were very piggy in their eating (picking the bones with their fingers etc.) and they had almost finished the Marsala. The old witch who sat at the head of the table tapped with her crooked-headed stick and removed her tall pointed hat. She had a hooky nose and chin and very bright eyes.

"Dear Pouncer is going to sing to us," another witch said.

"Hear, hear," the other witches said. "Dear Pouncer, sing."

"But you must join in the chorus, sisters. Shall it be the old song, dear Nightshade?"

"Yes, yes; the old song."

Mrs Pouncer cleared her throat and began:

> "When the midnight strikes in the belfry dark
> And the white goose quakes at the fox's bark,
> We saddle the horse that is hayless, oatless,
> Hoofless and pranceless, kickless and coatless,
> We canter off for a midnight prowl. . . ."

Chorus dear sisters. . . .

> "Whoo-hoo-hoo, says the hook-eared owl."

All the witches put back their heads to sing the chorus:

> "Whoo-hoo-hoo, says the hook-eared owl."

It seemed to Kay that they were looking straight at him. Nibbins' eyes gleamed with joy.

"I can't resist this song," he said. "I never could. It was this song, really, that got me into this way of life."

"But I don't know what it means. What is the horse that is hayless?"

"Aha," Nibbins said. "Well, we've time while they're at this song; it has nine times nine verses; but you ought to stay for some more Whoo-hoos. Doesn't it give you the feel of the moon in the tree-tops: 'Whoo-hoo-hoo, says the hook-eared owl?' Come along quietly."

Nibbins led the way up some more stairs, till he came to an open door, through which Kay saw the stars. "Why, this is the roof," he said. He saw how strange the roof was, close to, like this, with the twisted brick chimneys standing guard, with their cowls still spinning. He seemed very far from the ground.

"This is what they mean," Nibbins said. "Just open that middle chimney, will you?"

"But it is a chimney: it won't open."

"No, it isn't. There's a bobbin on it; pull that; it's their stable."

Kay scrambled up to the middle chimney of the three nearest to him. Sure enough, there was a bobbin on it. He pulled it, the latch came up, the chimney opened like a door; there inside was a cupboard in which stood one besom, one stable broom, one straw broom, one broom broom, and three kitchen brooms, each with a red head-stall marked with magic.

"Take the besom and the broom broom," Nibbins said, "and pitch the others over the gutter."

Kay pitched the five over the gutter; they whinnied as they fell on to the garden path, but nobody seemed to notice.

"Now let us mount and ride," Nibbins said. "But first, we'll shut the door."

He was going to shut the door into the house, when the noise of the song suddenly became much louder. Some-body at the banquet said "*Hush*" suddenly; the singing stopped, the witches were holding their door open, listening.

"They've heard us," Nibbins said. "Mount, Kay, and ride. Mount, catch him by the bridle, say *Sessa*, and point him where you want to go. Watch me."

Nibbins mounted the besom, Kay the broom broom. Just as he was mounted, he heard the sharp voice of Mrs Pouncer calling from the foot of the stairs.

> "Night-glider, tell . . .
> Are ill things well?"

Kay saw the besom toss up its head; it began to say:

> "Save, mistress, save,
> From white thief and black knave."

but before he could finish, both Nibbins and Kay said *Sessa* and pointed their horses towards the wood. Kay heard the witches clattering up the stairs on their high-heeled shoes. Looking back, he saw them all clustered on the roof shaking their fists and sticks, but already they were far away, for the two broom horses were rushing through the air so fast, that soon the house was out of sight. As they went over the elm boughs, they came so close to the top twigs, that some young rooks woke in the rookery and cried "Kaa" at them.

It was merry to be so high in the air. K. y could see the village with hardly a light in it, and the flashing of the brook where it went over the fall. Near the ponds, many little lights were twinkling. Kay wondered what they could be. A couple of white owls drifted up alongside Kay like moths; he could see their burning yellow eyes.

"We'll race you to the upper wood," they said.

"All right," Kay said. "Come up, horse."

The brooms were much faster than the owls: soon they were well ahead.

"You keep clear of Wicked Hill," the owls cried. They said something more, but the brooms were too far in front for the riders to hear.

"We'll land here, if you don't mind," Nibbins said. "I'd like to speak with a friend, if he's anywhere about. Point his head down to the quarry there."

When they had landed in the quarry, they tied the brooms to two spindle trees. "It must be spindle trees,"

Nibbins said. The quarry was bright in the moonlight and much overgrown with hazels and gorse.

"What is Wicked Hill?" Kay asked, "that we are to keep clear of?"

"They told us to keep clear of it, did they?" Nibbins said. "That shows there is something on. . . ."

FLYING WITH WITCHES

REIDAR THORWALD CHRISTIANSEN

On a farm in Ringebu there was a witch who was terribly mean. But there was a boy who knew she was a witch. He went there one Sunday evening and asked for a night's lodging, and he got it too.

"You mustn't be afraid if you see me sleeping with my eyes open," he said. "I'm in the habit of doing so, but I can't do anything about it!"

Oh, no, she would not be afraid of that, she said.

All at once he was snoring and sound asleep with his eyes open, and as he lay there like that, the woman took out a big horn of salve from under a stone in the hearth and annointed the broomstick.

"Up here and down here to Jönsås!" she said, and away she flew, up through the chimney, to Jönsås, which is a big mountain.

The boy thought it would be fun to follow her and see what she was going to do up there. But he thought she had said, "Up here and down here to mönsås!" (Mönsås means a crossbeam.) So he took out the horn from under the stone in the hearth and rubbed the salve on a piece of wood.

"Up here and down here to mönsås!" he said. Suddenly he began to fly up and down between the hearth and the crossbeam of the house. This kept up the whole night, and he was almost battered to death because he had said the wrong word. After that, he was given work there. A year later, on the evening of that very day, he was fixing a sled. When he got tired, he went over and lay down to sleep on the bench, staring straight ahead of him with his eyes open. All at once, the witch took out the horn from under the hearth and annointed the mop, and then she flew up through the chimney again. The boy watched where she had hidden the horn, and when she was well on her way, he took it and rubbed a little of the salve on the sled. But he did not say anything. The sled set out, and they never saw any more of the sled or the boy. The farm where this happened is called Kjæstad, and the Kjæstad Horn is renowned to this very day.

But then there was a woman on a farm at Dovre who was also a witch. It was a Christmas Eve. Her hired girl was busy washing a brewing vat. In the meantime, the woman took out a horn and annointed the broom, and all at once she flew up through the chimney. The girl thought this was quite a trick, and took out a little salve and rubbed it on the vat. Then she also set out, and did not stop until she came to Bluekolls (Blue Knoll.) There she met a whole flock of witches, and Old Erik himself. The Devil preached to them, and after he had finished, he looked to see if they had all come. Then he caught sight of the girl, who was sitting in the brewing vat. He did not know her, for she had not written in his book. And so he asked the woman, who was with her, if the girl would sign. The woman thought she would. Old Erik then gave the girl the book and told her to write in it. He wanted her to write her name, but she wrote what schoolchildren usually write when they try out their pens: "I am born of God in Jesus' name!" And then she was able to keep the book, for old Erik was not the one to touch it again.

Now there was an uproar and commotion upon the mountain, as you might know! The witches took whips and beat on whatever they had to ride on, and they set out helter-skelter. The girl did not wait; she also took a whip, beat on the vat, and set out after them. At one place they went down and rested on a high mountain. Far below them was a wide valley with a big lake, and on the other side was another high mountain. When the witches had rested, they laid on with the whips and swooped over the mountain. The girl wondered if she could also fly over it. At last she beat on the vat and came over on the other side too, both safe and sound.

"That was the devil of a hop for a brewing vat!" she said, but at that same moment she lost the book. And then she fell down and came no farther, because she had spoken and called him the devil, even though she had not written her name in the book. She had to go the rest of the way on foot, wading through the snow, for she did not get a free ride any more, and there was many a mile to go.

Revenge

THEOCRITUS translated by JACYNTH HOPE-SIMPSON

Simaetha goes to the crossroads, a traditional place for magic, to weave a spell upon Delphis, her faithless lover. Her maid, Thestylis, goes with her. As she says the spell, she spins a magic wheel (called a bird-wheel, because originally a wryneck was tied to it).

This is witchcraft in a very ancient form. Simaetha calls on the powers of the underworld and the moon. By her words she seeks to link herself with the great witch-priestesses, Medea and Circe. This poem is based on The Second Idyll *by Theocritus, who was born in Sicily, then a Greek colony, in about 310 B.C. Many later writers in different languages have imitated his poems about country life, but not all of them have made their characters seem as alive as Simaetha.*

Simaetha speaks to Thestylis

Quick, are the love charms and the bay leaves here?
Wreathe crimson knots around the bowl. I'll spell
A witch-charm on my love. He's not been near
My house for twelve whole days. He cannot tell
If I'm alive or dead. He's false. He's cruel.
Tomorrow I will ask him by what right
He treats me so. I'll go to the wrestling school
And see him.

But I'll weave a fire-spell tonight.
Moon, I mutter these words to you, so shine,

85

And I call to Hecate of the dead,
Of the dark earth. O let these words of mine
Be more fierce than Medea's, and more dread
Than Circe's were. Come, Mistress, hear my plea.
    O bird-wheel, wind him, wind him home to me.

First I'll burn barley. Thestylis, throw it round
As if you're scattering his bones upon the ground.
You slut, how dare you shrug with mockery?
    O bird-wheel, wind him, wind him home to me.

He tore my heart. I'll tear these leaves of bay
And burn them. See how fast they burn away.
So may his flesh be burnt in agony.
    O bird-wheel, wind him, wind him home to me.

I'll melt his waxen image over the fire.
May Delphis thus be melted by desire.
O magic bronze, make him tremble, twirl noisily.
    O bird-wheel, wind him, wind him home to me.

Goddess of hell, I know you're coming near
These crossroads. All the dogs are barking in fear
As you pass through the town mysteriously.
    O bird-wheel, wind him, wind him home to me.

They say this herb I hold drives horses mad.
Let it so madden Delphis; make me glad
When he comes running to me frenziedly.
    O bird-wheel, wind him, wind him home to me.

This fringe was once a part of Delphis' cloak,
I'll throw it now into the flames and smoke.

The dark blood of my love wells up, runs free . . .
  O bird-wheel, wind him, wind him home to me.

Tomorrow I'll brew poison for him. Here,
Thestylis, go to his house now and smear
His door with ashes. Curse him secretly.
  O bird-wheel, wind him, wind him home to me.
  Thestylis goes.

Once he would come three or four times a day,
As an excuse, he'd leave his flask behind.
But now, for all this time, he's stayed away:
There's someone else—I'm cast out of his mind.
I'll poison him, or else I'll put a spell
On him. If he won't love me, he shall die.
Tonight I'll try to bear the pain.
  Farewell
To the moon, to the powers of underworld and sky.

Some White Witchcraft

RUTH E. ST. LEGER-GORDON

As well as black magic, there is white: magic used for innocent purposes. A so-called "white-witch" is a healer. At one time, he or she may simply have been someone with a little more medical knowledge than other people. The term also means a man or woman who cures not by physical methods but by some form of thought-transference.

White witches seem to be most successful with minor ills, such as warts. Here are a few examples told by a writer who lives on Dartmoor in the present day, from her book The Witchcraft and Folklore of Dartmoor.

A farmer-neighbour, one of the most hard-headed, practical and sceptical men I have ever known, suffered from warts covering both hands. Out hunting one day, he happened to meet a noted wart-charmer who commented on the disfigurement, remarking casually: "I'll give 'ee halfpenny for 'em, boy!" The farmer merely laughed, but said he would accept the halfpenny, although he considered the man a "proper old fraud". The coin changed pockets, after which the farmer dismissed the incident altogether from his mind, until one day, to his surprise he found both hands clear of the warts from which he had suffered for so many years. He was sufficiently impressed to take his young daughter, similarly afflicted, to the same man, the result being equally successful. No question of faith entered this transaction—unless it was on

the part of the white witch. Until the accomplished cure of both himself and his daughter, the farmer remained sceptical throughout. After that, certainly, he became a reluctant convert.

Some witches advocate rubbing warts with bean-pods, others with bacon-rind. In each case, pods and rinds must be buried immediately after application. As they decay, so will the warts, the reasoning here presumably being based upon sympathetic magic. Results, however, appear to be completely satisfactory proving that the actual *methods* employed can have little or no bearing on the subsequent cure.

Counting plays a part in several of the methods used. By some witches the patient is instructed to go home, count his warts and put the equivalent number of small stones or pebbles into a bag which he must throw away, preferably at the cross-roads. I know a woman now about fifty, who, when in her twenties, adopted this procedure. At the time, she explained to me the danger of picking up any package found lying by the wayside. If, however, curiosity overcame caution, the packet should be kicked first to ascertain its contents, for should it contain "wart stones", the finder would automatically transfer to himself someone else's discarded warts.

One of the best wart-counting stories I have heard was told me by the daughter of an old-time squire. Both his hands had been peppered with persistent warts for years, every possible remedy having been tried unavailingly. Walking home from church one Sunday, he overtook an old village neighbour with whom he joined company. Presently, with characteristic directness, the old man commented on the squire's disfigurement. "How many warts have 'ee got then, zur?" he asked. The squire counted: "Twenty-seven." "They'll go," was the response, and no more was said on the subject. At home relating this incident to his wife, she exclaimed, "You haven't got as many warts as *that*, surely!" He counted again. "Actually, I've got one more," he said. "I told old Charlie twenty-seven, but it's twenty-eight."

Very shortly, twenty-seven warts had disappeared without trace. One remained.

The Bad Baronets

W. S. GILBERT

The witch's curse on the baronets of Ruddigore was that they should all do one bad deed every day. As the opera Ruddigore *shows, some of them found this difficult, as their ancestors' standard of badness was very high.*

Gilbert was the writing half of Gilbert and Sullivan, who together formed one of the most famous partnerships in the history of the theatre. It is always astonishing, listening to their operas, to think that the two men, whose music and words match so well, did not get on with each other.

Sir Rupert Murgatroyd
   His leisure and his riches
He ruthlessly employed
   In persecuting witches.
With fear he'd make them quake—
He'd duck them in his lake—
   He'd break their bones
   With sticks and stones,
And burn them at the stake!

   This sport he much enjoyed,
   Did Rupert Murgatroyd—
     No sense of shame
     Or pity came
   To Rupert Murgatroyd!

Once, on the village green,
    A palsied hag he roasted,
And what took place, I wean,
    Shook his composure boasted;
For, as the torture grim
Seized on each withered limb,
    The writhing dame
    'Mid fire and flame
Yelled forth this curse on him:

"Each lord of Ruddigore,
    Despite his best endeavour,
Shall do one crime, or more,
    Once, every day, for ever!
This doom he can't defy,
However he may try,
    For should he stay
    His hand, that day
In torture he shall die!"

The prophecy came true:
    Each heir who held the title
Had, every day, to do
    Some crime of import vital;
Until, with guilt o'erplied,
"I'll sin no more!" he cried,
    And on that day
    He said that say,
In agony he died!

And thus, with sinning cloyed,
Had died each Murgatroyd,
   And so shall fall,
   Both one and all,
Each coming Murgatroyd!

Once In, Never Out Again

AUSTRIAN FOLK TALE

Here is a traditional folk tale, with a witch, a princess, a dragon, and three brothers so alike that no one could tell which was which. It is an example of the stories, passed down by word of mouth for hundreds of years, that are now being written down before they die out altogether. Let us hope a few story-tellers will also survive to tell these tales, as they should be, out aloud.

ONCE upon a time there were three brothers called Hans, Sepp and Jorg. They were so alike that not even those who loved them best could tell one from the other. Shortly before their father died he sent them all out on their travels to seek their fortune. He gave each of them a knife. He told them to go together until they came to a lime-tree at a point where three roads branched off. Then they were all to take different ways. Before they parted, each was to bury his knife pointing along the road he intended to take. If any of them ever came back to the lime-tree, he was to look and see that his brothers' knives were all right. If one of the knives was rusty, it would be a certain sign that its owner was in trouble. The brothers said goodbye to their father, for the last time, as it turned out, and promised to do as he said.

They set out, and soon they came to the lime-tree. They all buried their knives, and then they went off, each taking a different way.

Hans, who was the eldest, took the road that went straight on. His first stop was at an inn. The innkeeper was very friendly, and, when Hans was leaving, he said he would give him a lion to go with him on his travels. He promised Hans that the lion was completely tame, and said that he was certain to find it useful. So Hans went on until he came to a town. The whole place was in mourning. Everybody looked miserable, and all the houses had black flags hung out of the bedroom windows. Hans went into the first inn that he came to, and after he had had something to eat, he asked the landlord what it was all about. The landlord said that a dragon, which lived in a gorge nearby, was terrorizing the town. The only way to keep him from killing everybody was to give him a young girl as his victim several times a year. But this had gone on for so long that now there were no more girls left in the town, except for the King's own daughter. Now she in her turn was to be delivered to the dragon. The only hope of escape was for someone to kill the dragon, but no one was brave enough.

As soon as he heard this, Hans decided to try. He asked the landlord to take him to see the King, and they went to the palace together. When they said why they had come, they were taken in to see the King straight away. Hans offered to fight the dragon, and asked if he could be given a good sword. The King was overjoyed. He not only gave Hans a sword, but said that he could marry the Princess if he succeeded.

Next morning, they set off for the gorge where the dragon lived. Hans was wearing his sword and the lion padded along by his side. It was very tame so far as he was concerned, but he hoped that it would be savage against the dragon. The Princess followed after them in a jet-black coach, so that she could be sacrificed to the dragon if Hans should fail. The townspeople watched them go. They were torn between hope that Hans would kill the monster, and fear that their princess would have to die after all.

When they got to the gorge, Hans started to clamber down to the dragon's lair. As he got near it he could hear the creature snorting away. Then it smelt them and came out, eager to have its feast. But as soon as it saw a man instead of a girl it flew into a terrible rage. It came charging towards them, breathing furiously. Hans snatched hold of his sword. He was quick on his feet and managed to dodge the monster. It charged him again, and again he leapt out of its way. Then, as it pulled up in confusion, he leant over and plunged his sword into its breast. Blood spurted out. Maddened with pain, the dragon reared up to pounce upon him. But just then the lion leapt up on its back. It seized hold of the loose skin on the dragon's neck in its teeth, and started to worry at it. The dragon tried in vain to shake this new enemy off. Once again, Hans plunged his sword into the dragon's breast. With these two wounds and the bites that the lion had inflicted, the dragon's strength ebbed quickly away, and it died.

Hans cut off the dragon's tongue as a proof that he had killed it. He ordered some men who had been watching, too frightened to join in the fight, to drag the beast back to the town. Then he went back to the Princess in her black coach. He made wreaths of wild flowers to put on the horses and on to the Princess's hair, to show everybody that they came back in triumph. They drove into the town.

Of course, the townspeople were all delighted, and so was the King. He said Hans could marry his daughter.

They had a magnificent wedding, and were very happy together. That ought to be the end of the story, and so it would be, if Hans had obeyed his wife.

One day, when they were out riding together, they came to a valley that Hans had not seen before. He asked his wife where it led, but all she would say was, "Once in, never out again." She would not tell him who lived there, or anything else about it. Hans decided to find out for himself. One day when the Princess was busy with something else, he set off. His only companion was the lion, who went everywhere with him.

When he got to the valley, his way was barred by a snake. He threw a stone at it, wounding it badly, and rode on. The valley twisted and turned, and at last he came to a castle. Nobody was about. He went in, but still there was no one. He walked through a hall of stone statues, shivering, because it was very cold. At the far end of the hall, a fire was laid in a large open fire-place. Hans lit it and sat

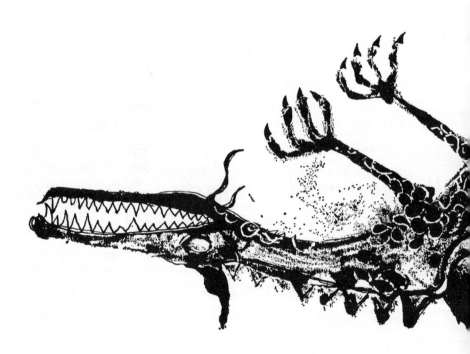

down to warm his hands. Soon an old woman came hobbling in, with a little stick in her hands. She said, "Brr! Isn't it cold?"

"Come and warm yourself," said Hans kindly.

The old woman came to the fire.

"Would you mind if I touch you and your lion with my little stick?" she asked.

"Do if you want to," said Hans.

She did so, and at that moment Hans and the lion were both turned into stone. They were nothing but two life-less statues among all the other stone statues in the big hall. For the old woman was really a wicked witch.

The poor Princess waited and waited and wondered what could have happened to Hans. At last she came to fear that he must be dead.

Meanwhile, Sepp, the second brother, had been having many adventures. At last, he came back to the lime-tree where he had left his two brothers. He dug up their knives to see if they were all right. Jorg's knife was still bright, but Hans's knife was eaten away with rust. Sepp knew that he must be in danger. So he in turn took the road that Hans had taken before. Like Hans, he stopped at an inn. Exactly the same thing happened, for, as he was leaving, the innkeeper gave him a tame lion to accompany him on his travels. They went on until they came to a town. Then Sepp, who was feeling hungry, turned in at the first inn he came to. It was, of course, the inn at which Hans had stopped. The landlord came hurrying out, half-happy and half-cross.

"Hans, where on earth have you been? Why didn't you tell us that you were going away? Hurry on up to the castle, the Princess will be delighted to see you."

Sepp was quick to realize what had happened. He and

his brothers had always been so alike that no one could tell them apart. But what had Hans been doing, and who was the Princess? He decided to let the landlord go on thinking that he was Hans, but he pretended that he had lost his memory. In this way, he got the landlord to tell him all he knew about Hans. Then he went on up to the castle. Not even the Princess realized that he was not Hans. At first she was angry with him for being away for so long, but very soon she forgave him. As for Sepp, he liked the Princess so much that he was happy to stay with her.

One day they went out riding and came to a narrow valley.

"Where does it go to?" asked Sepp.

The Princess looked at him in surprise, for she believed he had asked this question before.

"Once in, never out again," she replied, and that was all she would say.

Sepp was just as curious as his brother. He wanted to know more about this mysterious valley. At the first possible chance, he rode there without the Princess. He had only his lion for company. He saw a snake lying across the path to the valley. It was already badly wounded, so Sepp threw a stone at it and killed it. He rode on up the valley until he came to a castle. It seemed to be deserted. He went in and wandered through it until he came to the hall with stone statues. One of them, that was stretching out its hands as if to a fire, reminded him of his brother. Because he was cold, Sepp lit a fire himself.

A few minutes later, a little old woman came bustling in to the room. "Brr! Isn't it cold?" she said.

"Come to the fire," said Sepp.

"But I daren't."

"Why ever not?"

"Because of the lion, of course."

"Oh, he's a friendly lion," said Sepp. "Come here, and don't worry."

So the old woman came nearer. After a while, she said, "May I touch you and your lion with this little stick of mine?"

Sepp shook his head.

"I do so want to," she pleaded.

"Oh, very well then," said Sepp.

And before he knew what was happening, he and the lion were both turned into stone. The witch had two more statues in her collection. As for the poor Princess, she thought she had lost her husband all over again.

Now only Jorg, the youngest brother, was left. After many long journeys, he came back to the lime-tree where they had separated. First he looked for Sepp's knife, but it was no longer where he had buried it. Then he looked for Hans's knife. He found it where he expected, with Sepp's knife beside it, both pointing the same way. Both knives were very rusty. He knew this meant that Sepp had already come looking for Hans, and he knew that both his brothers must be in serious trouble. So he buried the knives again quickly, and then he too set off along the road that the others had taken before him. Like the others, he stopped at the inn where the innkeeper kept lions. He too was given a lion to go with him on his journey. He travelled on to the town. Because he was hungry he went into the first inn that he came to. The landlord came hurrying out. The three brothers were so alike that he naturally thought this was Hans come again. The lions, perhaps, were not quite so alike, but the landlord never went very close to them.

"This has gone past a joke," said the innkeeper angrily. "You can't keep on disappearing like this. The poor

Princess has been worried to death about you. You'd better go up to her straight away. And mind you don't disappear again. Things have been happening while you've been off on this jaunt of yours. For one thing I've been made a Minister of State. So I really know what's happening now. And let me tell you that the king is so old that we're going to have a new one. Who do you think it is? You! Just you get up to the castle and do your duty—and don't vanish again."

"But I don't understand," said poor Jorg. "Who do you think that I am?"

"Why, you're Hans, of course, and you might have the decency to explain why you've twice ridden off without so much as saying goodbye. And why you've come back both times without your horse as well."

In vain did Jorg try to explain that he was not Hans at all. The landlord would not believe him. They went up to the castle together, and the Princess, too, thought he was Hans come back. As for Jorg, when he saw the Princess, he decided that being Hans might have its compensations.

One day, the Princess and Jorg went out riding together.

"Where does this valley go to?" Jorg asked, as they came to the mouth of a valley.

"Once in, never out again," the Princess replied automatically. Then she looked at him crossly. "You've asked me that twice before, and I'll never tell you again."

Jorg was so puzzled by this that he thought he must come to the valley without the Princess. One day when she was busy he set out, alone except for his lion. He saw a dead snake lying across the path, and kicked it out of the way. At last he came to the castle. He got off his horse and went in. There was no one about at all. After a while he came to the hall with the statues. He saw that one looked like Hans and one looked like Sepp. He realized that somebody must have cast a spell on them both. He determined to try to lift it.

He sat down to wait, to see what was going to happen. It was cold, so he lit a fire in the large open fire-place. A few minutes later the witch came hobbling in.

"Brr! isn't it cold?" she said.

Jorg pretended to be friendly, as he wanted her to come nearer.

"Come and warm yourself by the fire."

"No, I'm frightened your lion will bite me!"

"He's never bitten anyone in his life."

So the witch came nearer to the fire.

"Would you mind if I touch you and the lion with my little stick? Not very hard, just to stroke you."

Now Jorg knew how the spell had been done. He leapt up and towered over her.

"You are a wicked witch! You have cast a spell on my brothers, and on all the others here. Take the spell off them at once. If you don't, I will order my lion to tear you up into pieces."

The lion gave an angry growl. The witch was so terrified that she scurried around the room and touched all the statues with her little stick. At once, they came back to life. Jorg and Hans and Sepp embraced one another warmly. All the others thanked Jorg for rescuing them.

They were all anxious to get away from the castle, and so they set off for the town, taking the witch as their prisoner. Hans, Sepp, and Jorg rode in front of the joyful procession. When they got to the town, everyone was astonished. Nobody could believe that three young men could be so alike.

The story ended happily for them all. Jorg was acclaimed as a hero. The innkeeper turned Minister adopted him as a son, for he had no son of his own. Sepp was given the witch's castle, and the valley "Once in, never out again." In the future it was a happy valley, where people came and went freely. Hans did best of them all, for he became King, and he got the Princess as well. She was delighted to have him back, this time for ever.

And the witch? Oh, the witch. She was burnt at the stake. So was the little stick, too.

The Powers of Witches

Now it is time for the witches to speak for themselves. These women actually lived.

Isobel Gowdie was a young Scotswoman, wife of a Morayshire farmer. In 1662 she amazed everyone, including her husband, by making a spontaneous confession that she was a witch. Why she did this, no one will ever know. Her confession has been called the most detailed account of witchcraft from the witch's point of view that we have. Under the laws of that time, she was then tried, and the full version of her confession can be found in Robert Pitcairn's Criminal Trials in Scotland.

Agnes Sampson was a "matron-like, grave" woman. She was accused with other witches of conspiring to kill the King, James VI of Scotland, at the time of his marriage in 1589. An anonymous writer told of her confession in News From Scotland, published two years later. This is an extract from it, slightly abridged.

Finally, the song which Agnes Sampson and her fellow-witches are supposed to have sung. The refrain "ring-a-ring a-widdershins" makes it sound like a children's dance; or perhaps it is the other way round, for some children's singing games are said to have come from witch dances.

A WITCH'S CONFESSION

ISOBEL GOWDIE

When we go in the shape of a hare, we say thrice over:

> I shall go intill a hare,
> With sorrow and sych and meikle care;
> And I shall go in the Devil's name
> Aye while I come home again.

And instantly we start in a hare.

The Devil would send me now and then to Aulderne on some errands to my neighbours, in the shape of a hare. I was one morning, about the break of day, going to Aulderne in the shape of a hare, and Patrick Papley's servants in Kilhill, being going to their labouring, his hounds being with them, ran after me, I being in the shape of a hare. I ran very long but was forced, being weary, at last to take to my own house. The door being left open, I ran in behind a chest, and the hounds followed in; but they went to the other side of the chest; and I was forced to run forth again, and won into another house, and there took leisure to say:

> Hare, hare, God send thee care.
> I am in a hare's likeness now,
> But I shall be a woman even now.
> Hare, hare, God send thee care.

And so I returned to my own shape, as I am at this instant again. The dogs will sometimes get bites of us, when we are in hares, but will not get us killed.

★

And when we take away the fruit of corn at Lammas, we take a wool-shear, and cut or clip away only three stalks of it, and plait other three reeds together, and say:

> We cut this corn in our Lord the Devil's name,
> And we shall have the fruit of it hame.

And say this thrice over, and so we have the fruit of that field. And we lay all up until Yule or Holy days; and part it among us, and feast on that together. . . .

And when we take away any cow's milk, we pull the tow and twine and plait it in the wrong way, in the Devil's name; and we draw the tedder (so made) in betwixt the cow's hinder feet, and out betwixt the cow's forder feet in the Devil's name, and thereby take with us the cow's milk. . . .

We took a thread of each colour of yarn that was in Alexander Cumming's dyeing-vat, and did cast three knots on each thread, in the Devil's name; and did put the threads in the vat, widdershins about in the vat, in the Devil's name; and thereby took the whole strength of that vat away, so that it could dye nothing but only black, according to the colour of the Devil, in whose name we took away the strength of the right colours that were in the vat. . . .

And when we took away the fruit of the fishes from the fishers, we went to the shore, before the boat would come in to it; and we would say, on the shore-side, three several times over:

> The fishers are gone to the sea,
> And they will bring home fish to me;
> They will bring them home intill the boat,
> But they will get out of them but the smaller sort.

And with that we have all the fruit of the whole fishes in the boat; and the fishes that the fishermen themselves will have, will be but froth.

TO KILL A KING

ANON

James VI of Scotland (later James I of England) was a well-known witch-hater and wrote a book called Demonology. *When he sailed home from Denmark with his Danish bride some Scottish witches conspired to kill him. Echoes of this story appear in* Macbeth, *as when the First Witch says, "In a sieve I'll thither sail."*

It has been suggested that this plot was engineered by Francis, Earl of Bothwell, who was believed to traffic in magic.[1]

Agnes Sampson, the eldest witch of them all, was after brought again before the King's Majesty and his Council, and being examined of the meetings and detestable dealings of those witches, she confessed that upon the night of All-Hallow Even last, she was accompanied with a great many witches, to the number of two hundred, and that all they together went to sea, each one in a riddle or sieve, and went into the same very substantially, with flagons of wine, making merry and drinking by the way in the same riddles or sieves, to the kirk of North Berwick in Lothian; and that after they had landed, took hands on the land and danced, singing all with one voice:

> Cummer go ye before, cummer go ye,
> If ye will not go before, cummer let me.

[1] If James had died without children, Bothwell might have come to the throne.

At which time she confessed that this Geillis Duncane did
go before them, playing this reel or dance upon a small
trump, called a Jew's trump, until they entered into the
kirk of North Berwick.

The said Agnes Sampson confessed that the devil, being
at North Berwick kirk, attended their coming in the habit
or likeness of a man. And having made his ungodly

exhortations, wherein he did greatly inveigh against the King of Scotland, he received their oaths for their good and true service towards him, and departed; which done they returned to sea and so home again.

Touching this Agnes Sampson, she is the only woman who, by the devil's persuasion, should have intended and put into execution the King's Majesty's death in this

manner. She confessed that she took a black toad and did hang up the same by the heels three days, and collected and gathered the venom as it dropped and fell from an oyster shell, and kept the same venom close covered, until she should obtain any part or piece of linen cloth that had appertained to the King's Majesty, as shirt, handkercher, napkin or any other thing. She practised to obtain these by means of one John Kers, attendant in His Majesty's chamber, and desired him for old acquaintance between them to help her to one, or such a piece of cloth as is aforesaid; which thing the said John Kers denied to help her, saying he could not. And the said Agnes Sampson saith that if she had obtained any one piece of linen cloth which the King had worn, she had bewitched him to death, and put him to such extraordinary pains, as if he had been lying upon sharp thorns and ends of needles.

Moreover, she confessed that at the time when His Majesty was in Denmark she, being accompanied by the parties before specially named, took a cat and christened it, and afterwards bound to each part of that cat the chiefest part of a dead man and several joints of his body. And she confessed that in the night following the said cat was conveyed into the midst of the sea by all these witches, sailing in their riddles or sieves, as is aforesaid, and so left the said cat right before the town of Leith in Scotland. This done, there did arise such a tempest in the sea, as a greater hath not been seen. This tempest was the cause of the perishing of a boat or vessel coming from the town of Brunt Island to the town of Leith, wherein was sundry jewels and rich gifts, which should have been presented to the now Queen of Scotland, at Her Majesty's coming to Leith. Again, it is confessed, that the said christened cat was the cause that the King's Majesty's ship, at his coming forth of Denmark, had a contrary wind to the rest of the ships then in his company, for when the rest of the ships had a fair and good wind, then was the wind contrary and altogether against His Majesty. Further, the said witch declared, that His Majesty had never come safely from the sea, if his faith had not prevailed against their intentions.

THE WITCHES' REEL

This is the song that the North Berwick witches sang as they danced. ("Cummer" was a Scottish word for addressing a woman, particularly a witch.)

Cummer go ye before, cummer go ye,
If ye willna go before, cummer let me,
   Ring-a-ring a-widdershins
   Linkin' lithely widdershins
Cummer carlin crone and queen
   Roun' go we!

Cummer go ye before, cummer go ye,
If ye willna go before, cummer let me,
   Ring-a-ring a-widdershins
   Loupin' lightly widdershins
Kilted coats and fleeing hair
   Three times three.

Cummer go ye before, cummer go ye,
If ye willna go before, cummer let me,
   Ring-a-ring a-widdershins
   Whirlin' skirlin' widdershins
And deil take the hindermost
   Who'er she be!

"The Witch's Curse"

LOUISA M. ALCOTT

Nearly all the problems familiar to amateur actors beset four sisters producing a Christmas play. From the way the girls talk and behave there is little to show that the period of this story is one hundred years ago at the time of the American Civil War. Little Women, *from which this story is taken, has been a success ever since it was first published in 1869. The character of Jo March, who is one of the outstanding creations in children's fiction, is said to be based on Louisa Alcott herself.*

The rehearsal.

"We must go shopping tomorrow afternoon, Meg; there is lots to do about the play for Christmas night," said Jo, marching up and down with her hands behind her back, and her nose in the air.

"I don't mean to act any more after this time; I'm getting too old for such things," observed Meg, who was as much a child as ever about "dressing up" frolics.

"You won't stop, I know, as long as you can trail round in a white gown with your hair down, and wear gold-paper jewellery. You are the best actress we've got, and there'll be an end of everything if you quit the boards," said Jo. "We ought to rehearse tonight; come here, Amy, and do the fainting scene, for you are as stiff as a poker in that."

"I can't help it; I never saw anyone faint, and I don't

114

choose to make myself all black and blue, tumbling flat as you do. If I can go down easily I'll drop; if I can't, I shall fall into a chair and be graceful; I don't care if Hugo does come at me with a pistol," returned Amy, who was not gifted with dramatic power, but was chosen because she was small enough to be borne out shrieking by the hero of the piece.

"Do it this way; clasp your hands so, and stagger across the room crying frantically, 'Roderigo! save me! save me!' " and away went Jo with a melodramatic scream which was truly thrilling.

Amy followed, but she poked her hands out stiffly before her, and jerked herself along as if she went by machinery; and her "Ow!" was more suggestive of pins being run into her than of fear and anguish. Jo gave a despairing groan, and Meg laughed outright, while Beth let the bread she was toasting burn as she watched the fun, with interest.

"It's no use! Do the best you can when the time comes, and if the audience shout, don't blame me. Come on, Meg."

Then things went smoothly, for Don Pedro defied the world in a speech of two pages without a single break; Hagar, the witch, chanted an awful incantation over her kettleful of simmering toads, with weird effect; Roderigo rent his chains asunder manfully, and Hugo died in agonies of remorse and arsenic, with a wild "Ha! ha!"

"It's the best we've had yet," said Meg, as the dead villain sat up and rubbed his elbows.

"I don't see how you can write and act such splendid things, Jo. You're a regular Shakespeare!" exclaimed Beth, who firmly believed that her sisters were gifted with wonderful genius in all things.

"Not quite," replied Jo modestly. "I do think 'The Witch's Curse, an Operatic Tragedy', is rather a nice thing; but I'd like to try *Macbeth*, if only we had a trap-door for Banquo. I always wanted to do the killing part. 'Is that a dagger that I see before me?'" muttered Jo, rolling her eyes and clutching at the air, as she had seen a famous tragedian do.

"No, it's the toasting fork, with ma's shoe on it instead of the bread. Beth's stage-struck!" cried Meg, and the rehearsal ended in a general burst of laughter.

The performance.

The morning charities and ceremonies took so much time, that the rest of the day was devoted to preparations for the evening festivities. Being still too young to go often to the theatre, and not rich enough to afford any great outlay for private performances, the girls put their wits to work, and necessity being the mother of invention, made whatever they needed. Very clever were some of their productions; pasteboard guitars, antique lamps made of old-fashioned butter-boats, covered with silver paper, gorgeous robes of old cotton, glittering with tin spangles from a pickle factory, and armour covered with the same useful diamond-shaped bits, left in sheets when the lids of tin preserve-pots were cut out. The furniture was used to being turned topsy-turvy, and the big room was the scene of many innocent revels.

No gentlemen were admitted; so Jo played male parts to her heart's content, and took immense satisfaction in a pair of russet-leather boots given her by a friend, who knew a lady who knew an actor. These boots, an old foil, and a slashed doublet once used by an artist for some picture, were Jo's chief treasures, and appeared on all occasions.

The smallness of the company made it necessary for the principal actors to take several parts apiece; and they certainly deserved some credit for the hard work they did in learning three or four different parts, whisking in and out of various costumes, and managing the stage besides.

On Christmas night, a dozen girls piled on to the bed, which was the dress circle, and sat before the blue and yellow chintz curtains, in a most flattering state of expectancy. There was a good deal of rustling and whispering behind the curtain, a trifle of lamp-smoke, and an occasional giggle from Amy, who was apt to get hysterical in the excitement of the moment.

Presently a bell sounded, the curtains flew apart, and the Operatic tragedy began.

"A gloomy wood", according to the one play-bill, was represented by a few shrubs in pots, a green baize on the floor, and a cave in the distance. This cave was made with a clothes-horse for a roof, bureaus for walls; and in it was a small furnace in full blast, with a black pot on it, and an old witch bending over it. The stage was dark, and the glow of the furnace had a fine effect, especially as real steam issued from the kettle when the witch took off the cover. A moment was allowed for the first thrill to subside; then Hugo, the villain, stalked in with a clanking sword at his side, a slouched hat, black beard, mysterious cloak, and the boots. After pacing to and fro in much agitation, he struck his forehead, and burst out in a wild strain, singing of his hatred for Roderigo, his love for Zara, and his pleasing resolution to kill the one and win the other. The gruff tones of Hugo's voice, with an occasional shout when his feelings overcame him, were very impressive, and the audience applauded the moment he paused for breath. Bowing with the air of one accustomed to public praise, he

stole to the cavern, and ordered Hagar to come forth with a commanding, "What ho! minion! I need thee!"

Out came Meg, with grey horse-hair hanging about her face, a red and black robe, a staff, and cabalistic signs upon her cloak. Hugo demanded a potion to make Zara adore him, and one to destroy Roderigo. Hagar, in a fine dramatic melody, promised both, and proceeded to call up the spirit who would bring the love philtre:

Hither, hither, from thy home,
Airy sprite, I bid thee come!
Born of roses, fed on dew,
Charms and potions canst thou brew?
Bring me here, with elfin speed,
The fragrant philtre which I need;
Make it sweet, and swift and strong;
Spirit, answer now my song!

A soft strain of music sounded, and then at the back of
the cave appeared a little figure in cloudy white, with
glittering wings, golden hair, and a garland of roses on its
head. Waving a wand, it sung:

Hither I come,
From my airy home,
Afar in the silvery moon;
Take the magic spell,
Oh, use it well!
Or its power will vanish soon!

and dropping a small gilded bottle at the witch's feet, the
spirit vanished. Another chant from Hagar produced
another apparition,—not a lovely one, for, with a bang, an
ugly black imp appeared, and having croaked a reply,
tossed a dark bottle at Hugo, and disappeared with a
mocking laugh. Having warbled his thanks, and put the
potion in his boots, Hugo departed; and Hagar informed
the audience that, as he had killed a few of her friends in
times past, she has cursed him, and intends to thwart his
plans and be revenged on him. Then the curtain fell, and
the audience reposed and ate candy while discussing the
merits of the play.

A good deal of hammering went on before the curtain

rose again; but when it became evident what a masterpiece of stage carpentering had been got up, no one murmured at the delay. It was truly superb! A tower rose to the ceiling; halfway up appeared a window with a lamp burning at it, and behind the white curtain appeared Zara in a lovely blue and silver dress, waiting for Roderigo. He came, in gorgeous array, with plumed cap, red cloak, chestnut love-locks, a guitar, and the boots, of course. Kneeling at the foot of the tower, he sung a serenade in melting tones. Zara replied, and after a musical dialogue, consented to fly. Then came a grand effect of the play. Roderigo produced a rope-ladder with five steps to it, threw up one end, and invited Zara to descend. Timidly she crept from her lattice, put her hand on Roderigo's shoulder, and was about to leap gracefully down, when, "alas, alas, for Zara!" she forgot her train,—it caught in the window; the tower tottered, leaned forward, fell with a crash, and buried the unhappy lovers in the ruins!

A universal shriek arose as the russet boots waved wildly from the wreck, and a golden head emerged, exclaiming, "I told you so! I told you so!" With wonderful presence of mind, Don Pedro, the cruel sire, rushed in, dragged out his daughter with a hasty aside,—

"Don't laugh, act as if it was all right!" and ordering Roderigo up, banished him from the kingdom with wrath and scorn. Though decidedly shaken by the fall of the tower upon him, Roderigo defied the old gentleman and refused to stir. This dauntless example fired Zara; she also defied her sire, and he ordered them both to the deepest dungeons of the castle. A stout little retainer came in with chains, and led them away, looking very much frightened, and evidently forgetting the speech he ought to have made.

Act third was the castle hall; and here Hagar appeared,

having come to free the lovers and finish Hugo. She hears him coming, and hides; sees him put the potions into two cups of wine, and bids the timid little servant, "Bear them to the captives in their cells, and tell them I shall come anon." The servant takes Hugo aside to tell him something, and Hagar changes the cups for two others which are harmless. Ferdinando, the "minion", carries them away, and Hagar puts back the cup which holds the poison meant for Roderigo. Hugo, getting thirsty after a long warble, drinks it, loses his wits, and after a good deal of clutching and stamping, falls flat and dies; while Hagar informs him what she has done in a song of exquisite power and melody.

This was a truly thrilling scene; though some persons might have thought that the sudden tumbling down of a quantity of long hair rather marred the effect of the villain's death. He was called before the curtain, and with great propriety appeared leading Hagar, whose singing was considered more wonderful than the rest of the performance put together.

Act fourth displayed the despairing Roderigo on the point of stabbing himself, because he has been told that Zara has deserted him. Just as the dagger is at his heart, a lovely song is sung under his window, informing him that Zara is true, but in danger, and he can save her if he will. A key is thrown in, which unlocks the door, and in a spasm of rapture he tears off his chains, and rushes away to find and rescue his lady-love.

Act fifth opened with a stormy scene between Zara and Don Pedro. He wishes her to go into a convent, but she won't hear of it; and, after a touching appeal, is about to faint, when Roderigo dashes in and demands her hand. Don Pedro refuses, because he is not rich. They shout and gesticulate tremendously, but cannot agree, and Roderigo is about to bear away the exhausted Zara, when the timid servant enters with a letter and a bag from Hagar, who has mysteriously disappeared. The latter informs the party that she bequeaths untold wealth to the young. pair, and an awful doom to Don Pedro if he doesn't make them happy. The bag is opened, and several quarts of tin money shower down on the stage, till it is quite glorified with the glitter. This entirely softens the "stern sire"; he consents without a murmur. all join a joyful chorus, and the curtain falls on the lovers kneeling to receive Don Pedro's blessing, in attitudes of most romantic grace.

Tumultuous applause followed, but received an unexpected check for the cot-bed on which the "dress circle" was built, suddenly shut up, and extinguished the entire audience. Roderigo and Don Pedro flew to the rescue, and all were taken out unhurt, though many were speechless with laughter. The excitement had hardly subsided when Hannah appeared, with "Mrs March's compliments and would the ladies walk down to supper."

Protection against Witches

The belief that plants have magical powers is extremely ancient. The charm tells how to cure a sudden pain caused by evil spirits. It was written down about nine hundred years ago in the language we call Anglo-Saxon or Old English, but the beliefs it expresses stretch back into the past, to the days before England became Christian.

Writing a thousand years later, Dorothy Jacob tells of other beliefs about plants, traces of which survive to the present day, in a book with the delightful title, A Witch's Guide to Gardening. *This extract is slightly abridged.*

A CHARM TO CURE A SUDDEN STITCH

translated by JACYNTH HOPE-SIMPSON

Take feverfew, and the red nettle that grows through the house, and dock. Boil them in butter.
Think of the evil spirits that caused the pain. Speak these words to command the stabbing spear of pain to go.

"Loud were the mighty women when they rode over
    the hill,
Bold were the mighty women when they rode over
    the land.
Defend yourself now to survive the attack.
    Out little spear, if you are herein!

I stood under a shield,
While the mighty women prepared their strength
And sent screaming spears.

124

I will send them back another,
An arrow hurtling towards them.
    Out, spear, not in, spear!"

Then say the words of the charm.

"If herein be a scrap of iron,
The work of a witch, it shall melt.
If you were shot in the flesh, if you were shot in
    the skin,
Or were shot in the blood, or shot in the bone,
Or were shot in a limb,
    Your life will come to no harm.
If it were the shot of gods, or the shot of elves,
Or it were the shot of a witch,
    I will give you help.
This will cure the shot of the gods,
This will cure the shot of elves,
This will cure the shot of a witch,
    I will give you help.

Flee, pain, to the mountain head!
Be whole. The Lord be your help!"

Then take the knife. Plunge it into the brew.

THE POWERS OF PLANTS AND TREES TO
PROTECT AGAINST WITCHES

DOROTHY JACOB

Heading the list of all protective plants is angelica. It is the
only plant, as far as I can discover, which was never used in

witchcraft. It was known as the Holy Ghost plant. Legend says its wonderful virtues were revealed to a monk, which is how it was given this name.

Ash was a marvellous protector. A wise man would always drive his cattle with an ash-plant to keep the witches off. I have sometimes asked myself if the collections of ash walking-sticks which one sees (or used to see) at the door of every small tobacconist, and from which I have had many in my time, are an unconscious relic of the belief that anyone carrying an ash stick was safe from the powers of evil. If you met a farmer walking over his fields today with a stick in his hand, you could make a pretty safe bet it would be of ash.

Even stronger as a witch-guard was the ash's younger brother rowan (mountain ash). After angelica, it was probably the strongest shield of all. Its red berries made it an additional weapon, as all red was held in abhorrence by witches.

> Their spells were vain. The hags returned
> To their queen in sorrowful mood,
> Crying that witches have no power
> Where thrives the rowan tree wood.
> (From the old ballad of the *Laidley Worm of Spindleston Heughs*.)

A sprig should always be kept at the head of the bed to scare off the witches. A rowan stake hammered into a corpse will keep its ghost quiet. Bewitched horses can only be controlled by a rowan switch. The staff to the churn, the mast of the ship should be made of its wood: A twist of it should be nailed over the cattle-shed door to keep the cattle safe from the mischief done by witches. It is as well to tie a piece to each cow's tail as an extra precaution. In different parts of England it has different names—Witch-wood, Quickbane, Wild Ash, Wichen, Witchbane, and many others.

A bay tree is another sure preserver. One should always be planted close to the house, for "Neither witch nor devil, thunder nor lightning will hurt a man in the place where the bay tree is".

The oak and the yew we know well as protectors. The birch had the same beneficence and it is wise to wear or carry a twig. In Hereford it was customary to place little crosses made of birch or rowan over the door of the house in May to ward off witches. Juniper has a very good reputation in every country. It is one of the trees always used to smoke out witches, probably, though perhaps unconsciously, because of its very pungent smell. It is very unlucky to cut one down. Bracken was considered holy because the marking on its roots when it was cut, were said to resemble the Greek letters for the name of Christ; this made it anathema to witches. A very strange protective plant in coastal districts was a certain seaweed known as "Lady's trees". Small dried branches hung in cottages would give protection against fire and evil spirits.

The Witch of Berkeley

WILLIAM OF MALMESBURY translated by J. A. GILES

We all know what happened in 1066. Here is something that happened in 1065. Or so William of Malmesbury firmly believed.

William of Malmesbury died in 1143. His Chronicle of The Kings of England *is one of the best early histories of this country. William took care to back up his facts. He knows that his tale of the Witch of Berkeley sounds very unlikely, but, he says, "I have heard it from a man of such character, who swore he had seen it, that I should blush to disbelieve." He also points out that "no person will deem this incredible who has read St. Gregory's dialogues."*

Today, we may have much stronger doubts about the truth of his story, but then we live in a very different world. What William might not have believed was that, near this same village of Berkeley in Gloucestershire, there would one day be a nuclear power station, and a road-bridge carrying cars over the Severn to Wales.

THERE resided in Berkeley a woman addicted to witchcraft, as it afterwards appeared, and skilled in ancient augury. On a certain day, as she was regaling, a jackdaw, which was a very great favourite, chattered a little more loudly than usual. On hearing which the woman's knife fell from her hand, her countenance grew pale, and deeply groaning, "This day," said she, "my plough has completed its last furrow; today I shall hear of and suffer some dreadful calamity."

While yet speaking, the messenger of her misfortunes arrived; and being asked, "why he approached with so distressed an air," "I bring news," said he, "from that village," naming the place, "of the death of your son, and of his whole family, by a sudden accident."

At this intelligence, the woman, sorely afflicted, immediately took to her bed, and perceiving the disorder rapidly approaching the vitals, she summoned her surviving children, a monk and a nun, by hasty letters; and when they arrived, with faltering voice, addressed them thus: "Formerly, my children, I have constantly administered to my wretched circumstances by demoniacal arts: yet while practising these crimes, I was accustomed to soothe my hapless soul with the hope of your piety. I advanced you as my defenders against evil spirits, my safeguards against my strongest foes. Now, since I have approached the end of my life, and shall have those eager to punish, who lured me to sin, I entreat you at least to endeavour to alleviate my torments. Although you cannot revoke the sentence already passed upon my soul, yet you may perhaps rescue my body by these means: sew up my corpse in the skin of a stag; lay it on its back in a stone coffin; fasten down the lid with lead and iron; on this lay a stone, bound round with three iron chains of enormous weight; let there be psalms sung for fifty nights, and masses said for an equal number of days, to allay the ferocious attacks of my adversaries. If I lie thus secure for three nights, on the fourth day bury your mother in the ground; although I fear, lest the earth, which has so often been burdened with my crimes, should refuse to receive and cherish me in her bosom."

They did their utmost to comply with her injunctions: but alas! vain were the pious tears, vows, or entreaties; so great was the woman's guilt, so great the devil's violence. For on the first two nights, while the choir of priests was singing psalms around the body, the devils, one by one,

with the utmost ease bursting open the door of the church,
though closed with an enormous bolt, broke assunder the
two outer chains; the middle one being more laboriously
wrought, remained entire. On the third night, about cock-
crow, the whole monastery seemed to be overthrown
from its very foundation, by the clamour of the approaching enemy. One devil, more terrible in appearance than
the rest, and of loftier stature, broke the gates to shivers by

the violence of his attack. The priests grew motionless with fear, their hair stood on end, and they became speechless. He proceeded, as it appeared, with haughty steps towards the coffin, and calling on the woman by name, commanded her to rise.

She replying that she could not on account of the chains: "You shall be loosed," said he, "and to your cost:" and directly he broke the chain, which mocked the ferocity of

the others, with as little exertion as though it had been made of flax. He also beat down the cover of the coffin with his foot, and taking her by the hand, before them all, he dragged her out of the church. At the doors appeared a black horse, proudly neighing, with iron hooks projecting over his whole back; on which the wretched creature was placed, and, immediately, with the whole party, vanished from the eyes of the beholders. Her pitiable cries, however, for assistance, were heard for nearly the space of four miles.

A Cat and a Broom

BARBARA SLEIGH

Rosemary's wish to earn some money during her holidays leads her to make two strange purchases, which are the starting point of many adventures. This extract from Carbonel *is the lighter side of witchcraft, set convincingly in the ordinary modern world.*

WHEN they had finished, Mrs Brown had to go into the town to match some silks, so Rosemary cleared away and washed up the dinner plates. Next she put away her school things and changed into a cotton frock, and all the time she was wondering what she could do with herself for the next three weeks. Could she really do something useful, she wondered, as Mrs Walker, the landlady, had suggested? It had been rather unfair to call her a "great girl", because she was rather small for her ten years. All the same, it would be wonderful, she thought, to earn some money without her mother knowing anything about it, and at the end of the holidays carelessly to pour a shower of clinking coins into her astonished lap!

"The trouble is, I don't know what I could do," she said to herself. "I can't sew well enough. The only thing I can do is to keep our rooms clean and tidy. I always do that in the holidays when Mummy is busy. I can sweep and polish and wash-up."

She rather liked the idea, and by the time she had done

up the difficult button at the back of her cotton frock Rosemary had made up her mind. She would go out daily and clean.

Now she had a hazy idea that it would be necessary to take her tools with her, in the same way that her mother took her own thimble, needles, and scissors when she went out to sew. Dusters and a scrubbing brush would be easy, but Mrs Walker would not let her past the front door with a broom without going into a long explanation, and then it would no longer be a surprise.

"Well, there is nothing for it," she said to herself, "I shall have to buy one for myself."

After much rattling and poking with a dinner knife her money-box produced two and fivepence three farthings.

"P'r'aps if I went to Fairfax Market I could find a cheap broom," she thought doubtfully. "It's rather a long way, but I think I could get there and back before tea-time."

Rosemary put the money in her pocket and left a note for her mother; then she started off for Fairfax Market. This was held in the old part of the town in the cobbled market square. Because she imagined that two and fivepence three-farthings was not very much money with which to buy a broom, she decided not to waste any of it on a bus.

She started resolutely off, only stopping occasionally to look in a shop window. But it was hot and dusty going. The pavements seemed to toast the soles of her feet through the rubber soles of her sandals. To make matters worse, one of the buckles came off. By the time she reached the market a slight drizzle was falling, and the clock on the Market Hall roof was striking four. Instead of the cheerful racket of people shouting their wares, of laughter and bustle, the stall-holders were already packing up. Rosemary went up to a stout woman who was stacking crockery which had been displayed on the cobbles.

"Please," she said anxiously, "will you tell me where I can buy a broom?"

"You can't," snapped the fat woman without looking up. "Not now you can't." Then she straightened herself with a grunt and looked at Rosemary's disappointed face.

"Never ask a favour of a fat woman when she's bending," she said more kindly. "Leastways, not if you want a civil answer. Don't they teach you that at school?"

Rosie shook her head, and the fat woman went on, "The market's been closing at four on Mondays these last three 'undred years, leastways, so my old father told me. Never mind, cheer up, lovely! 'Ave a fancy milk jug for your ma instead?"

Rosemary shook her head again and went sadly on between the rows of dismantled stalls and piles of goods hidden under tarpaulins, already glistening with rain. The money in her hand was hot and sticky, but there was nothing to buy with it, let alone a broom, so she put it back in her pocket. She inquired again of a young man who was loading bales of brightly coloured material into an ancient car.

"Please, do you know where I can buy a broom?"

But all he said was "'Op it, see?" So Rosemary 'opped it.

She wandered on among the drifting straw and bits of paper till she came to the end of the market, where the pavement began again. Here she found a little shop that sold newspapers and sweets and odds and ends, so she stopped to look in the window. She wondered whether to buy a toffee-apple or a liquorice bootlace to sustain her on the way home. The toffee-apple would last longer, but on the other hand she could eat a bit of the bootlace and use the rest as a skipping rope and still eat it later. She had just decided on the apple, because you cannot skip comfortably with the buckle off your sandal, when she felt something damp and furry rubbing against her bare legs. She looked down, and saw a huge black cat. Now Rosemary liked cats. If only Mrs Walker had allowed it she would certainly have had one of her own, so she bent down to stroke him. But the cat ran off and then sat down a few yards away and looked at her. Rosemary followed and tried to stroke him again, but the creature darted off for a few feet as before, and sat down to wash its paws. Rosemary laughed.

"I believe you want me to follow you! All right, I will. I'm coming!" So they went off in fits and starts, with Rosemary trying to catch the cat, who lolloped away as soon as she was within striking distance. But although the cat did not laugh as she did, it was perfectly obvious that he was enjoying the joke as much as she was. She was just going to make a successful grab at him when she bumped into someone. It was an old woman.

"I'm so sorry!" said Rosemary.

"And so you should be," said the old woman sharply, "keeping me waiting like this. Well, it's yours for two and fivepence, and it's cheap at the price."

"What is?" asked Rosemary in a puzzled way.

"The broom, of course! That's what you've come for, isn't it? If that cat is trying to fool me just because I'm going out of business. . . ."

The cat was patting a drifting piece of orange paper with deep concentration.

"Oh, but I do want a broom !" said Rosemary eagerly.

"I've sold my stock and bought myself a new hat," went on the old woman unexpectedly. "How do you like it?"

Rosemary hoped she would not be asked to give an opinion about any of the rest of the old woman's clothes. The hat was certainly very fashionable. It was sprinkled with sequins and had a little veil. But perched on the old woman's wild grey hair it only served to make the hair look wilder and her ragged clothes more disreputable.

"It's very pretty," said Rosemary. "But shall I take off the price label? It's hanging down behind."

"Oh, no you don't!" said the old woman fiercely. "I paid nineteen and elevenpence for my hat and I'm not giving away any of the trimmings! You can have the broom and the cat, too, if you like, but my trimmings aren't in the bargain."

Rosemary felt quite indignant at the turn the conversation was taking and she answered with some spirit.

"Of course I don't want the trimmings from your hat! But I wish I could have the cat." She looked at the handsome animal who was sitting with his tail neatly curled round his feet, apparently fast asleep.

The old woman chuckled. "He's a deep one, he is!" She paused, looked sharply at Rosemary and added, "He's worth his weight in . . . farthings."

"But if the broom costs two and fivepence I've only got three farthings left, and he must be worth much more than that!" Surely Mrs Walker could be talked round? Anyway she knew that her mother would not mind. It was more than likely that the queer old woman was not a very kind mistress. Rosemary had a feeling that the cat was not really asleep, but was listening with all his ears.

"You can have him for three farthings if that is all you've got," said the old woman.

"I'll have him!" she answered breathlessly. As she said it, the cat opened his eyes, flashed one golden glance at her, and closed them again.

Rosemary pulled the money out of her pocket and put it into the not too clean hand which the old woman was already greedily holding out for it. She counted eagerly, but it was the farthings that seemed to interest her most. She held them up to her short-sighted eyes, then she bit them and chuckled.

"I guessed as much. You're in luck, my boy. Three queens for a prince!"

"They are my Queen Victoria farthings. That's why I kept them. They are all I have. Will they do?"

"Oh, aye, they'll do better than you know," replied the old woman.

The cat was not pretending to sleep now. He was wide awake and staring at Rosemary with his two great golden eyes. "You can take him," she went on, and prodded him with her foot. "And don't say I never did you a good turn, my boy. Though, mind you, it's only half undone."

The Market Hall clock struck five as she spoke.

"It's getting awfully late," said Rosemary. "I think I must be going. Please may I have the broom?"

"The broom? Oh, aye, here you are." And so saying the old woman pushed it into Rosemary's hand, turned and disappeared down a dark alley at the side of the sweet shop. As she went under the arch she ducked her head as if she was used to a much taller kind of hat.

Rosemary watched her go. Then she looked down at the broom, and her heart sank. It was not what she wanted at all. It was the sort of broom that gardeners use—a rough wooden handle with a bundle of twigs bound on at one end, and only a few dilapidated twigs at that.

"What a shame!" said Rosemary. As the full extent of her bad luck dawned on her she could not stop the hot tears from trickling down her face. The broom was useless, at least for her purpose. She had no money left to buy another, and to crown it all she would have to walk all the way home without a buckle on her shoe, with not even the consolation of a toffee-apple. However, she was a brave little girl, and in the absence of a handkerchief she wiped her eyes with the back of her hand and decided to make the best of it. But just at that moment, quite clearly and distinctly, the cat said:

"It's a better bargain than it looks, you know."

"Who said that?" Rosemary could not believe her ears.

"Me, of course!" said the cat. "Oh, yes, of course I can talk. All animals can, but you can only hear me because you are holding the witch's broom."

Rosemary dropped it hurriedly. Then, realizing that she could not hear the cat talk without it, she picked it up again.

"And I should treat it with respect," went on the animal dryly. "There's not much life in the poor thing or she would not have sold it so cheap. Trust her for that! Pity you didn't hear some of the things I said to her just now!" he went on with satisfaction. "Not names; that is vulgar, but I tickled her up nicely!" and his tail twitched at the memory.

Rosemary remembered how the queer old woman had known, without being told, exactly how much money she had.

"But is she really a witch?" she whispered in an awed voice.

"Hush!" said the cat, hurriedly looking over his shoulder. "Best not to use that word. She was, right up to the moment when you bought me and the broom. Now she's retired; says she's going to turn respectable." He added scornfully, "A fish might as well say it's decided not to swim. You haven't such a thing as a saucer of milk about you?"

Rosemary shook her head. "Pity. *You-Know-What* have their uses. *She* could always produce a saucer of milk no matter where we were, in the middle of Salisbury Plain or playing catch-as-catch-can with the Northern Lights."

"That was kind of her, anyway," said Rosemary.

"Not so very," said the cat. "If she was in a bad temper, which she generally was, like as not it would be sour."

"Well, as soon as we get home you shall have as much milk as you can drink. But I'm afraid we shall have to walk.

I haven't any money for a bus fare. Besides, I don't know whether they let cats go on buses."

"Then go by broom," said the cat.

"By broom?" said Rosemary, feeling rather puzzled.

"I wish you wouldn't keep repeating everything," snapped the cat. "Mind you, it won't fly very high. You couldn't expect it, not in the state the poor thing is in now. But it will take us there all right. Well, go on, why don't you mount?"

"Mount?" said Rosemary.

"There you go again! It is quite simple. You just stand astride it and say where you want to go. Best do it in rhyme. It is more polite, and the poor thing is sensitive now it is so old."

"There is not much to rhyme with Ten Tottenham Grove, top floor," said Rosemary doubtfully.

"Leave it to me," said the cat. "Tottenham Grove . . . stove . . . mauve . . . I've got it. Not very polished, but it will serve. Now then, mount and hold tight!"

He balanced himself delicately on the twiggy part of the broom. "Now repeat after me!"

> Through window wide and not the door,
> Ten Tottenham Grove, the topmost floor!

As Rosemary repeated it there was a faint quiver in the handle of the broom, and it rose slowly a couple of feet from the ground, wheeled sharply round, so that Rosemary nearly fell off, and went steadily on in the direction of Tottenham Grove. On it went, ignoring traffic lights, skimming zebra crossings, and leaving a train of astonished pedestrians in its wake. At first Rosemary could do nothing but shut her eyes and clutch the handle and pray that she would not fall off. But the motion was smooth and pleasant and she became aware that the cat was telling her something, so she opened her eyes.

"I . . . I'm afraid, I did not hear what you said."

"I was saying," said the cat, "that you should always point your broom in the direction in which you want to go. I knew a young witch once who was thrown."

"Goodness!" said Rosemary. "What did she do?"

"Nothing. There was not much she could do. It got clean away. Nasty things, runaway brooms, apart from the expense of getting a new one, and the trouble of breaking it in."

By now Rosemary was beginning to enjoy herself. She knew that cars were not supposed to do more than thirty miles an hour when driving through a town, and as they steadily overtook everything else on the road she said to herself: "Perhaps it doesn't apply to witch's brooms."

A policeman outside the Town Hall tried to hold them up before he realized what she was riding. His astonishment when he did realize so staggered him that he quite lost his head, and the traffic jam that resulted gave Rosemary a clear road to the corner of Tottenham Grove.

When they neared number ten she had enough sense to hold on for all she was worth. The broom gathered itself together for a tremendous effort, rose steeply, swooped into her bedroom window, and collapsed exhausted on the floor. Rosemary stood up and rubbed her elbow. Then she picked up the broom again.

"Best hide it in the wardrobe," said the cat.

"Thank you, Broom!" she whispered, and stood it in the corner behind her winter coat. She could hear her mother using the sewing-machine next door.

Weather-Witches—Two Points of View

The idea that magic can be used to affect the weather is very ancient indeed. When belief in witchcraft was widespread, it was thought that witches had the power to cause storms. Here is the popular opinion—and the other point of view.

BELIEF

In the History of Travel in the West and East Indies *(1577), Richard Eden describes how Finnish witches sell winds. Similar stories are told of the Isle of Man in the fourteenth century by Ranulf Higden; and in 1814, Sir Walter Scott, out of curiosity, bought a wind from a woman in Stromness in Orkney.*

They tie three knots on a string hanging at a whip. When they loose one of these, they raise tolerable winds. When they loose another, the wind is more vehement. But by loosing the third, they raise plain tempests, as in old time they were accustomed to raise thunder and lightning.

The Italian friar, Francesco-Maria Guazzo, had no doubts about the power of witches when he wrote his Compendium Maleficarum *(1626).*

Witches have confessed that they make hailstorms at the sabbat, or whenever they wished to blast the fruits of the earth. To this end, according to their confessions, they beat water with a wand, and then they threw into the air or into the water a certain powder which Satan had given them. By this means, a cloud was raised which afterwards turned to hailstones and fell wherever the witches wished.

AND DISBELIEF

In the Discovery of Witchcraft *(1584) Reginald Scot, of Kent, had the distinction of being the first writer to question the then widespread belief in witchcraft.*

No one endued with common sense but will deny that the elements are obedient to witches, and at their command-ment, or that they may, at their pleasure, send rain, hail, tempests, thunder, lightning, when she, being a doting old woman, casteth a flint stone over her left shoulder towards the west, or hurleth a little sea-sand up into the element, or wetteth a broom-sprig, and sprinkleth the same into the air; or diggeth a pit in the earth, and putting water therein stirreth it about with her finger; or boileth hog's bristles; or layeth sticks across upon a bank where never a drop of water is; or buryeth sage till it be rotten; all which things are confessed by witches, and affirmed by writers to be the means that witches use to move extraordinary tempests and rain.

This is what George Fox, founder of the Society of Friends, told "seafaring men" in 1676.

Let New England professors (of religion) see whether or no they have not sometimes cast some poor simple people into the sea on pretence of being witches. . . . For you may see that it was the Lord who sent out the wind and raised the storm in the sea, and not your witches, or ill-tongued people, as you vainly imagine.

Tam O'Shanter

ROBERT BURNS

The poem, Tam O'Shanter, of which the main part is given here, was written all at one sitting. It may be this which gives it its liveliness and excitement; the tremendous sense of movement in the witches' dance and in their wild chase after Tam.

This account of how Tam, having drunk too much, spies on the local witches, is often reckoned to be the greatest poem of Scotland's greatest poet. The lines move with a swing that carries the reader along. On first reading, at any rate, it is best not to pause too long over the odd unfamiliar word, but rather to enjoy the pace of the poem and Burns' masterly mixture of comic realism and the macabre. This version has deliberately been shortened and the spelling slightly modified to make it easier for those who have not read Burns before, but anyone who enjoys the story can find the full poem in his Collected Works.

> But to our tale: one market night
> Tam had got planted unco right
> Fast by an ingle, blazing finely,
> Wi' reaming swats,[1] that drank divinely;
> And at his elbow, Souter[2] Johnny,
> His ancient, trusty, droughty crony.
> The Souter told his queerest stories;
> The landlord's laugh was ready chorus;
> The storm without might roar and rustle,
> Tam did na mind the storm a whistle.

[1] foaming ale.   [2] Cobbler.

Nae man can tether time or tide;
The hour approaches Tam must ride;
And such a night he takes the road in
As ne'er poor sinner was abroad in.

The wind blew as 'twould blawn its last;
The rattling show'rs rose on the blast;
The speedy gleams the darkness swallow'd;
Loud, deep, and lang the thunder bellow'd:
That night a child might understand
The Deil[3] had business on his hand.

Weel mounted on his grey mare, Meg,
A better never lifted leg,
Tam skelpit[4] on thro' dub[5] and mire,
Despising wind, and rain, and fire;

[3] the Devil.   [4] rattled.   [5] puddle.

Whiles glow'ring round wi' prudent cares
Lest bogles[6] catch him unawares:
Kirk-Alloway was drawing nigh,
Where ghosts and owlets nightly cry.

The lightnings flash frae pole to pole;
Near and more near the thunders roll:
When, glimmering thro' the groaning trees,
Kirk-Alloway seem'd in a bleeze;
Thro' ilka bore[7] the beams were glancing;
And loud resounded mirth and dancing.

Inspiring bold John Barleycorn!
What dangers thou canst make us scorn!
The swats sae ream'd in Tammie's noddle,
Fair play, he car'd na deils a boddle.[8]
But Maggie stood right sair astonish'd,
Till, by the heel and hand admonish'd.
She ventured forward on the light;
And, vow! Tam saw an unco sight!

Warlocks and witches in a dance;
Nae coltillion brand-new frae France;
But hornpipes, jigs, strathspeys and reels,
Put life and mettle in their heels.
A winnock-bunker[9] in the east.
There sat auld Nick, in shape o' beast;
A towzie tyke,[10] black, grim and large,
To gie them music was his charge:
He screw'd the pipes and made them skirl

[6] hobgoblins.   [7] every cranny.   [8] i.e. he was too drunk to care
[9] window-recess.   [10] shaggy dog.

Till roof and rafters a' did dirl.[11]
Coffins stood round, like open presses,
That shaw'd the dead in their last dresses;
And, by some devilish cantrip sleight,[12]
Each in its cauld hand held a light—
By which heroic Tam was able
To note upon the holy table
A murderer's bones in gibbet-airns[13]
Twa span-lang, wee, unchristen'd bairns;
Wi' mair of horrible and awefu'
Which ev'n to name would be unlawfu'.

As Tammie glowr'd, amaz'd and curious,
The mirth and fun grew fast and furious:
The piper loud and louder blew,
The dancers quick and quicker flew:
They reel'd, they set, they cross'd, they cleekit[14]
Till ilka carlin sweat and reekit[15]
And cast her duddies[16] to the work
And linket[17] at it in her sark.[18]
Now Tam, O Tam! had they been queans[19]
A' plump and strapping in their teens!
Their sarks, instead o' greasy flannen,
Been snow-white seventeen hunder linen![20]—
These breeks o' mine, my only pair,
That once were plush, o' gude blue hair,
I would hae gi'en them off my hurdies[21]
For one blink o' the bonnie birdies!

[11] vibrate.   [12] weird trick.   [13] irons.
[14] took hands.   [15] each witch-steamed.
[16] clothes.   [17] set to it.   [18] petticoat.
[19] young women.   [20] very fine linen.   [21] buttocks.

But wither'd beldames, auld and droll,
Rigwoodie[22] hags would wean a foal,
Leaping and flinging on a crummock,[23]
I wonder didna turn thy stomach.

But Tam kenned what was what fu' brawlie:[24]
There was one winsome wench and wawlie,[25]
Her cutty sark,[26] o' Paisley harn,[27]
That while a lassie she had worn,
In longitude tho' sorely scanty,
It was her best, and she was vauntie.—[28]
Ah! little kenned thy reverend grannie,
That sark she bought for her wee Nannie,
Wi' twa pound Scots ('twas a' her riches),
Would ever grac'd a dance of witches!

But here my Muse her wing must cour[29]
Such flights are far beyond her power;
To sing how Nannie leaped and flang
(A souple jade she was and strang),
And how Tam stood like one bewitch'd
And thought his very e'en enriched;
Till first one caper, then anither,
Tam lost his reason a'togither
And roars out, "Weel done, Cutty-sark!"
And in an instant all was dark;
And scarcely had he Maggie rallied,
When out the hellish legion sallied.

[22] withered.
[24] quite well.
[26] short shift.
[28] proud of it.

[23] stick.
[25] comely.
[27] linen.
[29] fold.

As eager runs the market-crowd,
When "Catch the thief!" resounds aloud;
So Maggie runs—the witches follow,
Wi' many an eldritch[30] screech and hollow.

Ah, Tam! Ah, Tam! thou'll get thy fairin![31]
In hell they'll roast thee like a herrin!
Now, do thy speedy utmost, Meg,
And win the key-stone of the brig;
There, at them thou thy tail may toss:
A running stream they dare not cross.
But ere the key-stone she could make,
The fient a tail she had to shake![32]
For Nannie, far before the rest,
Hard upon noble Maggie prest,
And flew at Tam wi' furious ettle:[33]

But little wist she Maggie's mettle—
One spring brought off her master hale,
But left behind her ain grey tail:
The carlin[34] caught her by the rump,
And left poor Maggie scarce a stump.

Now, wha this tale o' truth shall read,
Ilk man and mother's son, take heed:
Whene'er to drink you are inclined,
Or cutty sarks run in your mind,
Think! ye may buy the joys o'er dear,
Remember Tam O'Shanter's mare.

[30] frightful.   [31] reward.
[32] she had no tail.   [33] endeavour.
              [34] witch.

Witch Hunts—The Aftermath

Witch hunts reached their height in the sixteenth and seventeenth centuries. The methods used to prove that people were witches, and the ways of extorting confessions from them, were ugly and vicious. Sir Walter Scott called them "a dark chapter in human nature".

It is not surprising that educated people should have reacted against this. But in country districts, memory lingered on. Long after the witch scare had died down, the old methods of "proving" a witch were still used occasionally. The last of these extracts shows a desire to test a witch in the old way, but to do it all "decent" and "not to hurt her".

REACTION

SAMUEL BUTLER

Matthew Hopkins was the most notorious of English witch finders. In 1645 and 1646 he accused hundreds of people in Eastern England of being witches. Public opinion then turned against his methods. This is what Samuel Butler said about him in Hudibras *(1664), a poem which satirises the self-righteous.*

And has not he, within a year,
Hanged three score of them in one shire?
Some only for not being drowned;
And some for sitting above ground
Whole nights and days upon their breeches,
And feeling pain, were hanged for witches.

And some for putting knavish tricks
Upon green geese and turkey chicks,
Or pigs that suddenly deceased
Of griefs unnatural, as he guessed.

MEMORY

One supposed mark of a witch was that she should weigh less than a church bible. Another was that she should float if thrown into water. Here are two examples of these beliefs surviving in the eighteenth and nineteenth century.

From *The Gentleman's Magazine,* 1759.

One Susannah Haynokes, an elderly woman, of Wingrove, near Aylesbury, Bucks, was accused by a neighbour for bewitching her spinning-wheel, so that she could not make it go round, and offered to make oath of it before a magistrate; on which the husband, in order to justify his wife, insisted on her being tried by the church Bible, and that the accuser should be present. Accordingly she was conducted to the parish church, where she was stripped of all her clothes, to her shift and undercoat, and weighed against the Bible; when, to the no small mortification of the accuser, she outweighed it and was honourably acquitted of the charge.

From *The Times,* April 3rd, 1857.

I send you the particulars of an application made to myself, as a magistrate, for an order to have a witch "proved". All written down by me at the time. . . .

November 17, 1856

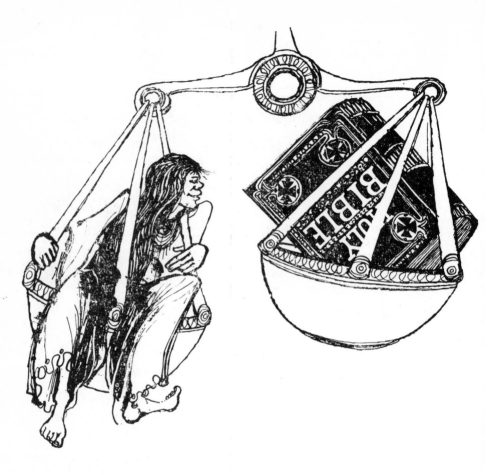

J.B. who farms about 40 acres makes application to Mr —, a magistrate, as follows:

J.B. Your worship, I come to ask you advice concerning of my wife.

Mr — What's the matter?

J.B. Why, your worship, she's harassed about night and day—continual worrying—like a wind teasing her stomach, and like a sow with all her young pigs a-pulling her to pieces.

Mr — I don't see what I can do for that. Why don't you send for a doctor?

J.B. Doctor, sir? We've been to all the doctors about.

We've spent every shilling to get remedy. . . . We're wholly done up.

Mr — Still, I don't see how I can help you.

J.B. Well, sir, it's thought by many people in the parish that my wife's bewitched; that it's put upon her by evil-disposed persons through envy. There's a family named L—, who got turned out when we was put in, and we think it's through them that they set old Mrs C. to do it. . . . She's an old woman, your worship, who live near the Lion, and she have the character of being a witch, and I thought I'd step down and ask your worship whether you would give me a grant to have her proved.

Mr — How is she to be proved?

J.B. Why, sir, I thought you could have her swum. I've heard say that, if they be witches, they won't sink. I've heard say that there was a gentleman . . . who had one swum in the river. I don't know exactly how it finished, but I've heard she didn't live long after it. He had it done right public. Her name was Pointer. They tied her clothes about her legs and used her decent. She had a line put round her waist, and one on each side, to keep her from sinking if she was an upright woman; but if she's a witch, they can't sink her no how. Old Mr L—, who done it, jumped upon her, but couldn't sink her no how; when her head was down her heels was up, and when her heels was down her head was up. . . . I do hope your worship will grant the police to take old Mrs C. of a sudden—by surprise like—and take her to a pit and swim her (not to hurt her). If she's an upright woman she'll sink, and if she don't sink it'll prove her guilty.

Fereyel and Debbo Engal the Witch

A Gambian Folk Tale told by
KATHLEEN ARNOTT

Fereyel is a very small boy with a very great deal of liveliness, cunning and daring. His story is told in African Myths and Legends. *It is appropriate to include a story from Africa in a book about witches, for an active belief in witchcraft still lives on in many places there.*

A LONG time ago there lived a witch called Debbo Engal. She had ten daughters, who were beautiful girls whom all men sought after, and from time to time youths would make the long journey to the house where they lived, hidden away in the bush. But none of these young men ever returned to their villages again, although nobody knew the reason why. Debbo Engal knew, however. When young men called to see her lovely daughters she would pretend to be delighted to meet them, giving them palm wine to drink and serving them choice food until night fell. Then she would say:

"It is too late and the night is too dark for you to walk back to your homes through the bush. Why not stay the night here and then go home at daybreak in safety?"

The young men would gladly agree, and Debbo Engal would tell them to lie down around the fire she kept burning in the biggest hut in the compound, and soon all would be asleep.

The wicked witch would then sharpen her large knife, creep up to the lads and kill them silently one by one with the skill of long practice. Then in the morning she would eat them! Debbo Engal did not feed on rice or corn or yams. Only human flesh satisfied her cruel appetite.

Now in a village some miles away lived a woman who had ten sons, and they heard of the beauty of Debbo Engal's daughters and wanted to visit them. Their mother entreated the boys not to go.

"It is an evil compound. Keep away, my sons," she begged. "So many young men have gone, never to return, and I do not want to lose all my sons at once."

But the lads laughed at her fears and assured her that they could look after each other and that ten men would be a match for any woman. Besides, the daughters were said to be so very beautiful that none of the young men could rest until they had seen the maidens.

Early the next morning the ten brothers set off in high spirits, singing and laughing as they walked along the narrow paths which led through the bush to Debbo Engal's compound.

No sooner had they left their mother, than she gave birth to an eleventh son. But what a strange-looking child he was, being scarcely the size of his mother's little finger. Then he stood upright straight away, and spoke to her.

"Good mother," he said, his bright little black eyes gazing fixedly at her face, "where are my brothers?"

"They have gone to Debbo Engal's compound," she replied in amazement, wondering how it was that he knew he had any brothers.

At this, the little boy gave a shout, exclaiming:

"Then I must go after them to save them," and he ran swiftly down the path which his brothers had taken.

Very soon he saw the ten lads in the distance and called after them:

"Hey! Hey! Wait for me."

The brothers stopped and turned to see who was calling and when the tiny boy ran up to them, they stared open-mouthed. Presently one of them managed to say:

"Who are you, and what do you want?"

"My name is Fereyel, and I am your youngest brother," he replied.

"Indeed you are not, for there are only ten of us," they replied. "Now go away and leave us in peace."

"I want to come with you to save you from harm," said Fereyel.

At this the brothers were angry and began to beat him, saying:

"Don't be so silly! How can you be our brother? Now go away and leave us in peace."

They beat him so hard that he lay senseless on the ground, and then the unkind brothers went on their way towards Debbo Engal's home.

Some time later one of the brothers found a piece of beautiful cloth lying across the path.

"Look what I've found!" he exclaimed. "Some careless person has dropped this fine cloth. This really is a lucky journey, isn't it?"

He picked up the cloth, slung it over his shoulder, and continued on his way. But somehow the cloth seemed to get heavier and heavier and presently he said to the second brother:

"Will you carry this for me? It is so very heavy on mv shoulder."

The second brother laughed at him for a weakling, but very soon he too found the cloth too heavy and passed it on to the third, and so it went on until it reached the eldest of the ten brothers. When he complained about the weight a shrill voice from inside the cloth called out:

"I'm inside! That's why you find the cloth so heavy. It is Fereyel, your youngest brother."

The young men were furious, and shaking Fereyel out of the cloth, they beat him again and again until once more they left him lying senseless beside the path.

"That's the end of him," they said. "Lying little scoundrel."

So they went on their way, for it was a long journey, and they began to hurry since they had wasted some time in beating Fereyel. Suddenly one of the brothers kicked his toe against a piece of metal, and as he bent to pick it up he saw that it was a silver ring.

"What luck!" he exclaimed. "Somebody has dropped a ring and now it is mine," and placing it on his finger he swaggered happily along. But after a few minutes his hand hung heavily at his side and it was all he could do to walk, so weighty had the ring become. Then the same thing happened with the ring as with the cloth, each brother taking turns to wear it but passing it on when it got too heavy until at last it reached the eldest.

"There's something odd about this ring," he said, and was just taking it off his finger when Fereyel's voice piped up saying:

"I'm inside! That's why it's so heavy," and he jumped out of the ring on to the ground.

The brothers were about to beat him again when the eldest said:

"He seems determined to follow us and he's certainly been very cunning about it. Leave him alone and let him follow us to Debbo Engal's place after all."

So on they went, until at last they reached the compound they were seeking and Debbo Engal came out to greet them.

"Welcome," she cried, "welcome to our home! Come and meet my daughters."

The ten girls were very lovely and the brothers could scarcely take their eyes away from them. They were led away to the largest hut and Debbo Engal brought them delicious food and drink. At first she did not see Fereyel, for he was hidden behind the eldest brother's foot, but suddenly she caught sight of him, picked him up and exclaimed:

"What a charming little fellow you are! Come with me to my hut, and I will see that you are properly looked after. Never have I seen anyone so tiny! You must stay with me and be mine."

The brothers were surprised when Fereyel allowed himself to be led away without protest, but they soon forgot all about him as they feasted and drank and danced with the ten beautiful girls.

Night came and the brothers talked about going home, but Debbo Engal persuaded them to stay where they were.

"There is no moon," she said, "and you might lose your way. There are many snakes and wild animals about at this season, too, so stay with us and return to your home by daylight tomorrow."

The lads needed little persuasion and soon began another dance, while Debbo Engal brought more palm wine to refresh them. At last, however, the ten boys and girls had to admit that they were too tired to stay awake any longer, and Debbo Engal lent the brothers some mats and pillows on which to rest in the large hut where the girls were already almost asleep.

The wicked witch went back to her hut and gave Fereyel a comfortable mat to sleep on, and a specially soft pillow for his head.

"There you are!" she said. "Go to sleep now, and do not wake until the morning. I shall sleep on the mat beside you, my little man, so you'll be quite safe."

So saying, she lay down and closed her eyes and soon the compound was wrapped in silence.

Presently Debbo Engal sat up and bent over Fereyel to see if he was asleep. He closed his eyes and kept perfectly still. She stood up and went to the corner where she kept her big knife, but just as she was taking hold of it, Fereyel called out:

"What are you doing?"

Hastily replacing the knife, Debbo Engal said sweetly:

"Aren't you asleep yet, little man? Let me smooth your pillow for you," and she tidied his bed, shook up the pillow and begged him to sleep in peace.

Once again she lay down beside him, and once again Fereyel pretended to sleep, so that after an hour the wicked witch got up for the second time and took out her knife, ready to sharpen it.

"What are you doing?" called Fereyel again; so making some excuse, Debbo Engal came back to her bed and told him to go to sleep again.

For a long time after that all was quiet, but Fereyel did not sleep. He waited until the steady breathing of the woman on the mat beside him told him that she was asleep, then silently he crept out of the hut, and made his way to where his brothers and the ten beautiful maidens were.

Gently and silently he changed all their clothes, putting the white gowns the boys wore over the girls, and covering his brothers in the blue robes of the women. Then he returned to Debbo Engal's hut, lay down again and waited.

Sure enough, Debbo Engal soon woke with a start, and for the third time she crept to the corner of her hut, seized her knife and began to sharpen it. Fereyel didn't interrupt her this time, and she slipped out of the door, holding the gleaming blade in her hand. Stealthily she entered the young people's hut, bent over the ten sleeping forms wrapped in white clothes and cut their throats with practised skill.

"Ah ha! They'll make me a splendid meal tomorrow," she muttered to herself as she lay down contentedly and fell asleep again.

As soon as he was sure Debbo Engal would not wake, Fereyel hurried into the big hut and shook each of his brothers by their shoulders.

"Get up! Get up!" he whispered. "Debbo Engal meant to kill you all, and had I not changed over your clothes she would have done so. Look!" and he pointed to the ten girls who lay with their throats cut. "The old witch thinks it is you she has killed."

The brothers needed no second bidding but tumbled hastily out of the door and began their journey home through the bush, anxious to get as far away from Debbo Engal as possible, before she woke up again.

But it was no use. As soon as the witch woke and discovered that Fereyel was no longer by her side, she rushed into her daughters' hut and saw that she had killed them by mistake in the darkness. Uttering a fearful cry, she called up the wind, mounted on its back and flew towards the brothers, who were as yet scarcely half-way home.

Fereyel saw her coming. "Look out!" he shouted to his brothers. "Here comes the old witch."

The brothers were panic-stricken but Fereyel knew

what to do. Seizing a hen's egg from under a bush, he dashed it on to the ground between them and Debbo Engal. The egg immediately turned into a wide, deep river and the young men were able to continue on their way.

Debbo Engal was furious and turned about at once and made for home. But the brothers had not got rid of her so easily, for she came back with her magic calabash and began to empty out all the water from the swiftly-flowing river. Soon there was not a drop left and she was able to continue her journey once more.

Fereyel saw her coming and shouted:

"Look out! Here comes the old witch again," while he seized a large stone and flung it in her path. Immediately it changed into a high mountain and the brothers continued on their journey, certain that Debbo Engal could not get them now.

But the witch was not defeated yet. She went back to her home on another puff of wind and fetched her magic axe. Then she hacked and chopped and chopped and hacked, until at last the whole mountain disappeared and she was able to continue on her way.

But she was too late. Just then Fereyel saw her coming again and gave his brothers a warning shout.

"Look out!" he cried, as they saw their village ahead, and with one final effort they reached their house. Debbo Engal knew she could not touch them there, and went away defeated, muttering fearful curses under her breath.

But Debbo Engal did not let the matter rest there. She was determined to get hold of the young men and kill them, even as she had mistakenly killed her own daughters, so she lay in hiding and waited her chance.

Early next morning the village headman told the brothers

to go into the bush and collect logs. Somewhat fearfully, they went, keeping close together and glancing over their shoulders from time to time in case the witch turned up again. They did not see her however, for the very good reason that she had heard the headman's instructions and had immediately turned herself into a log of wood.

As the lads collected the logs they stacked them beside the path.

"Come on," one of them called to Fereyel. "Don't be so lazy! Why are you standing still while we do all the work?"

"Because Debbo Engal has turned herself into a log, and I do not want to be the one who picks her up," he explained.

On hearing this, the brothers threw down the logs they were carrying and raced for home. Debbo Engal, who was furious that she had not yet been picked up, changed herself back into a witch and hid in the bush, still longing for revenge.

A few days later the brothers went off into the bush to collect wild plums. At first they only found trees with somewhat withered fruit, but suddenly they came upon a bush with bright green leaves and luscious, juicy plums hanging from its branches.

"Look at this! What luck!" exclaimed the eldest brother, reaching out his hand to pluck the fruit.

"Stop!" commanded Fereyel. "Don't you realize that it's a magic tree, and Debbo Engal is inside it? If you fill your calabashes with the fruit, she'll soon have you under her spell."

The brothers dropped their calabashes and ran home with haste, and once again Debbo Engal's plans were frustrated.

The next morning when the brothers came out of their compound, they saw a grey donkey grazing on the communal grass at the edge of the village. It seemed to belong to no one and the brothers thought it must have strayed from a nearby village.

"What luck," said the eldest. "Let's all have a donkey ride!"

One by one they climbed onto the donkey's back, until all ten of them were perched up there precariously. Then they turned to Fereyel standing beside them and called:

"Room for one more. Jump on!"

"There's no room at all," replied Fereyel. "Even I, small as I am, could not get on that donkey's back now."

Immediately the strangest thing happened. The donkey began to grow longer, and there was plenty of room for Fereyel.

"Ah ha!" he shouted. "You won't catch me climbing on the back of such an elongated donkey."

Then much to everyone's surprise, the donkey shrank back to its normal size.

Fereyel laughed. "You have all been tricked again," he said. "Donkeys don't usually understand what human beings are saying. But this one does, so it must be Debbo Engal again. Get off, if you value your lives!"

The brothers tumbled off the donkey's back and the animal went braying back to the bush, where it changed into Debbo Engal.

Now the witch was desperate. She had tried all her magic tricks save one, and she was determined to make this a success. "If I can only catch Fereyel, I shall be sure of the others," she said to herself, and sat in deep contemplation planning another wicked scheme.

The next morning a beautiful maiden walked into the village. The villagers crowded round her and asked why she had come.

"I want to see Fereyel," she replied in a clear bell-like voice. "Will you lead me to his house?"

Fereyel was amazed to see such an attràctive girl, and asked her to come into the visitors' hut. Then he went out and killed a young goat and told his mother to cook the meat for his beautiful guest.

All day long he entertained the maiden, giving her delicious food to eat and talking to her all the while. The villagers, who had never seen such beauty before, came peeping into the hut from time to time and went away exclaiming loudly at the wonderful sight.

When evening came the maiden said she must go back to her home.

"Will you lead me through the bush, Fereyel?" she asked. "It is too dark for me to go alone."

Fereyel willingly agreed and the whole village turned out to bid them good-bye. It was very dark and Fereyel led the way along the little winding path that the maiden had told him led to her home. Suddenly she disappeared behind a thick tree-trunk, and was completely hidden. Fereyel stood still, alert and waiting, straining his eyes in the dark.

Then out slithered a horrible, fat python which made straight for Fereyel and would have coiled itself round him and crushed him to death had he not been waiting for this moment.

"Aha! Debbo Engal," he laughed, and changed himself into a roaring fire. The python had no time to turn round. It could not stop its huge, rippling body from dashing straight into the fire, where it immediately perished.

Great was the joy in Fereyel's village when he went home and told his brothers the tale, and great was the feasting and dancing they had that night to celebrate the death of the wicked witch, Debbo Engal.

"*The Witch of Endor*"

From THE FIRST BOOK OF SAMUEL

One of the most famous of all witches is the woman known as "the Witch of Endor". In fact, she was not really a witch so much as a medium, who could communicate with the spirits of the dead. Saul, King of Israel, went to her for this reason. He was being attacked by his enemies and he was distressed because God did not answer his prayers.

This passage tells how the woman of Endor called up the spirit of the prophet, Samuel. Samuel told Saul that he had lost the favour of God, and warned him that he and his sons would soon die. This came true.

Saul lived nearly three thousand years ago. The characters in this story come across this vast space of time as real and living people. It is easy to imagine the "witch" herself. First she was scared that Saul was trying to trick her into breaking the law. Then, after she had exercised her strange powers, she turned into any ordinary housewife, fussing over Saul who had not had enough to eat.

NOW Samuel was dead, and all Israel lamented him, and buried him in Ramah, even in his own city. And Saul had put away those that had familiar spirits, and the wizards, out of the land. And the Philistines gathered themselves together, and came and pitched in Shunem: and Saul gathered all Israel together, and they pitched in Gilboa. And when Saul saw the host of the Philistines, he was afraid, and his heart greatly trembled. And when Saul enquired of the Lord, the Lord answered him not, neither by dreams, nor by Urim, nor by prophets.

Then said Saul unto his servants, "Seek me a woman

that hath a familiar spirit, that I may go to her and enquire of her."

And his servants said to him, "Behold, there is a woman that hath a familiar spirit at Endor."

And Saul disguised himself, and put on other raiment, and he went, and two men with him, and they came to the woman by night: and he said, "I pray thee, divine unto me by the familiar spirit, and bring me him up, whom I shall name unto thee."

And the woman said unto him, "Behold, thou knowest what Saul hath done, how he hath cut off those that have familiar spirits, and the wizards, out of the land: wherefore then layest thou a snare for my life to cause me to die?"

And Saul sware to her by the Lord, saying, "As the Lord liveth, there shall be no punishment happen to thee for this thing."

Then said the woman, "Whom shall I bring up unto thee?"

And he said, "Bring me up Samuel."

And when the woman saw Samuel, she cried with a loud voice: and the woman spake to Saul saying, "Why hast thou deceived me? for thou art Saul."

And the king said unto her, "Be not afraid: for what sawest thou?"

And the woman said unto Saul, "I saw gods ascending out of the earth."

And he said unto her, "What form is he of?"

And she said, "An old man cometh up: and he is covered with a mantle." And Saul perceived that it was Samuel, and he stooped with his face to the ground, and bowed himself.

And Samuel said to Saul, "Why hast thou disquieted me to bring me up?"

And Saul answered, "I am sore distressed; for the Philistines make war against me, and God is departed from me, and answereth me no more, neither by prophets, nor by dreams: therefore I have called thee, that thou mayest make known unto me what I shall do."

Then said Samuel, "Wherefore then dost thou ask of me, seeing the Lord is departed from thee, and is become thine enemy? And the Lord hath done to him, as he spake by me: for the Lord hath rent the kingdom out of thine hand, and given it to thy neighbour, even to David: because thou obeyedst not the voice of the Lord, nor executest his fierce wrath upon Amalek, therefore hath the Lord done this thing unto thee this day. Moreover the Lord will also deliver Israel with thee into the hands of the Philistines: and tomorrow shalt thou and thy sons be with me: the Lord shall also deliver the host of Israel into the hands of the Philistines."

Then Saul fell straightway all along on the earth, and was sore afraid, because of the words of Samuel: and there was no strength in him; for he had eaten no bread all the day, nor all the night. And the woman came unto Saul, and saw that he was sore troubled, and said unto him, "Behold, thine handmaid hath obeyed thy voice, and I have put my life in my hand, and have hearkened unto thy words which thou spakest to me. Now therefore, I pray thee, hearken thou also unto the voice of thine handmaid, and let me set a morsel of bread before thee; and eat, that thou mayest have strength when thou goest on thy way."

But he refused, and said, "I will not eat."

But his servants, together with the woman, compelled him; and he hearkened unto their voice. So he arose from the earth, and sat upon the bed. And the woman had a fat calf in the house; and she hasted, and killed it, and took flour and kneaded it, and did bake unleavened bread thereof; and she brought it before Saul, and before his servants; and they did eat. Then they rose up, and went away that night.

The Power of Thought

GERALD GARDNER

During the last few years, some light has been cast upon witchcraft by the reve-
lations of those who claim to be witches themselves. The best known of these is
the late Gerald Gardner, whose work has caused much controversy, not only in
the world at large, but, it is said, among witches.

The purpose of much modern writing about witchcraft is to show that the
cult is separate from Christianity, not a mockery of it. In this passage from
Witchcraft Today, *published in 1954, Gerald Gardner tells how witches*
have tried to use the concentrated power of thought for the good of their country.

WITCHES did cast spells, to stop Hitler landing
after France fell. They met, raised the great cone
of power and directed the thought at Hitler's
brain: "You cannot cross the sea. You cannot cross the sea.
Not able to come. Not able to come," just as their great-
grandfathers had done to Boney[1] and their remoter fore-
fathers had done to the Spanish Armada with the words:
"Go on. Go on. Not able to land. Not able to land." Is that
allying themselves with the King's enemies? I am not
saying that they stopped Hitler. All I say is that I saw a very
interesting ceremony performed with the intention of
putting a certain idea into his mind, and this was repeated
several times afterwards; and though all the invasion barges

[1] Napoleon Bonaparte.

were ready, the fact was that Hitler never even tried to come. The witches told me that their great-grandfathers had tried to project the same idea into Boney's mind.

At the time of the Spanish Armada the invading force was off the coast before the cult really heard about it. They knew it was useless trying to get at King Philip; he was out of touch with and could not change the Armada's course, and they had not the slightest idea who was in command. The only thing they could do was to send out a general idea: "Go on. Go on. Go on. You cannot land. You cannot land," and hope it would take effect. If they could have raised a storm, they would have done so, but they did not know how, though naturally they would pray to their gods to bring disaster to the fleet and this would probably include storms.

The Queen of Underland

C. S. LEWIS

Jill and Scrubb have escaped from their horrible school, Experiment House, to the magic of Narnia. Aslan, the mighty lion, has set them the task of finding Rilian, the king's only son, who has disappeared. His disappearance may be connected with a woman in green, perhaps the one who, in the form of a serpent, killed his own mother.

The two children take with them on their search, a Marsh-wiggle, that is a web-footed man, called Puddleglum. In the course of their adventures they leave the Overworld and go down to Underland in the depths of the earth. There they find Rilian, bound to The Silver Chair *that gives the book its title. In the name of Aslan they free him from the spell that the witch-queen of Underland has put on him. But still they need to defeat the witch-queen herself.*

The late C. S. Lewis was a distinguished scholar who wrote lively and original books on English literature and on religion. Of his children's books, the Chronicles of Narnia, he said, "I wrote the books I should have liked to read." He also said, "A children's book is the best art form for something you have to say." That is why The Queen of Underland *is an allegory: a story with two meanings. It can be read for its own sake as a very good story about a witch. We can also take the witch to stand for all the powers of evil, and Puddleglum's splendid defiance of her to stand for a faith in goodness, even at moments when all seems confused and hopeless.*

TWO Earthmen entered, but instead of advancing into the room, they placed themselves one on each side of the door, and bowed deeply. They were followed immediately by the last person whom anyone had expected or wished to see: the Lady of the Green Kirtle, the

Queen of Underland. She stood dead still in the doorway, and they could see her eyes moving as she took in the whole situation—the three strangers, the silver chair destroyed, and the Prince free, with his sword in his hand.

She turned very white; but Jill thought it was the sort of whiteness that comes over some people's faces not when they are frightened but when they are angry. For a moment the Witch fixed her eyes on the Prince, and there was murder in them. Then she seemed to change her mind.

"Leave us," she said to the two Earthmen. "And let none disturb us till I call, on pain of death." The gnomes padded away obediently, and the Witch-queen shut and locked the door.

"How now, my lord Prince," she said. "Has your nightly fit not yet come upon you, or is it over so soon? Why stand you here unbound? Who are these aliens? And is it they who have destroyed the chair which was your only safety?"

Prince Rilian shivered as she spoke to him. And no wonder: it is not easy to throw off in half an hour an enchantment which has made one a slave for ten years. Then, speaking with a great effort, he said:

"Madam, there will be no more need of that chair. And you, who have told me a hundred times how deeply you pitied me for the sorceries by which I was bound, will doubtless hear with joy that they are now ended for ever. There was, it seems, some small error in your Ladyship's way of treating them. These, my true friends, have delivered me. I am now in my right mind, and there are two things I will say to you. First—as for your Ladyship's design of putting me at the head of an army of Earthmen so that I may break out into the Overworld and there, by main force, make myself king over some nation that never did me wrong—murdering their natural lords and holding their throne as a bloody and foreign tyrant—now that I know myself, I do utterly abhor and renounce it as plain villainy. And second: I am the King's son of Narnia, Rilian, the only child of Caspian, Tenth of that name, whom some call Caspian the Seafarer. Therefore, Madam, it is my purpose, as it is also my duty, to depart suddenly from your Highness's court into my own country. Please it you to grant me and my friends safe conduct and a guide through your dark realm."

Now the Witch said nothing at all, but moved gently across the room, always keeping her face and eyes very steadily towards the Prince. When she had come to a little ark set in the wall not far from the fireplace, she opened it, and took out first a handful of a green powder. This she threw on the fire. It did not blaze much, but a very sweet and drowsy smell came from it. And all through the conversation which followed, that smell grew stronger, and filled the room, and made it harder to think. Secondly, she took out a musical instrument rather like a mandolin. She began to play it with her fingers—a steady, monotonous thrumming that you didn't notice after a few minutes. But the less you noticed it, the more it got into your brain and your blood. This also made it hard to think. After she had thrummed for a time (and the sweet smell was now strong) she began speaking in a sweet, quiet voice.

"Narnia?" she said. "Narnia? I have often heard your Lordship utter that name in your ravings. Dear Prince, you are very sick. There is no land called Narnia."

"Yes there is, though, Ma'am," said Puddleglum. "You see, I happen to have lived there all my life."

"Indeed," said the Witch. "Tell me, I pray you, where that country is?"

"Up there," said Puddleglum, stoutly, pointing over-head. "I—I don't know exactly where."

"How?" said the Queen, with a kind, soft, musical laugh. "Is there a country up among the stones and mortar of the roof?"

"No," said Puddleglum, struggling a little to get his breath. "It's in Overworld."

"And what, or where, pray is this . . . how do you call it . . . Overworld?"

"Oh, don't be so silly," said Scrubb, who was fighting hard against the enchantment of the sweet smell and the thrumming. "As if you didn't know! It's up above, up where you can see the sky and the sun and the stars. Why, you've been there yourself. We met you there."

"I cry you mercy, little brother," laughed the Witch (you couldn't have heard a lovelier laugh). "I have no memory of that meeting. But we often meet our friends in strange places when we dream. And unless all dreamed alike, you must not ask them to remember it."

"Madam," said the Prince sternly, "I have already told your Grace that I am the King's son of Narnia."

"And shalt be, dear friend," said the Witch in a soothing voice, as if she was humouring a child, "shalt be king of many imagined lands in thy fancies."

"We've been there, too," snapped Jill. She was very angry because she could feel enchantment getting hold of her every moment. But of course the very fact that she could still feel it, showed that it had not yet fully worked.

"And thou art Queen of Narnia too, I doubt not, pretty one," said the Witch in the same coaxing, half-mocking tone.

"I'm nothing of the sort," said Jill, stamping her foot. "We come from another world."

"Why, this is a prettier game than the other," said the Witch. "Tell us, little maid, where is this other world? What ships and chariots go between it and ours?"

Of course a lot of things darted into Jill's head at once: Experiment House, her own home, radio-sets, cinemas, cars, aeroplanes, queues. But they seemed dim and far away. (Thrum, thrum, thrum, went the strings of the Witch's instrument.) Jill couldn't remember the names of the things in our world. And this time it didn't come into her head that she was being enchanted, for now the magic was in its full strength; and of course, the more enchanted you get, the more certain you feel that you are not enchanted at all. She found herself saying (and at the moment it was a relief to say):

"No. I suppose that other world must be all a dream."

"Yes. It is all a dream," said the Witch, always thrumming.

"Yes, all a dream," said Jill.

"There never was such a world," said the Witch.

"No," said Jill and Scrubb, "there never was such a world."

"There never was any world but mine," said the Witch.

"There never was any world but yours," said they.

Puddleglum was still fighting hard. "I don't know rightly what you all mean by a world," he said, talking like a man who hasn't enough air. "But you can play that fiddle till your fingers drop off, and still you won't make me forget Narnia; and the whole Overworld too. We'll never see it again, I shouldn't wonder. You may have blotted it out and turned it dark like this, for all I know. Nothing more likely. But I know I was there once. I've seen the sky full of stars. I've seen the sun coming up out of the sea of a morning and sinking behind the mountains at night. And I've seen him up in the midday sky when I couldn't look at him for brightness."

Puddleglum's words had a very rousing effect. The other three all breathed again and looked at one another like people newly awaked.

"Why, there it is!" cried the Prince. "Of course! The blessing of Aslan upon this honest Marsh-wiggle. We have all been dreaming, these last few minutes. How could we have forgotten it? Of course we've all seen the sun."

"By Jove, so we have!" said Scrubb. "Good for you, Puddleglum! You're the only one of us with any sense, I do believe."

Then came the Witch's voice, cooing softly like the voice of a wood-pigeon from the high elms in an old garden at three o'clock in the middle of a sleepy, summer afternoon; and it said:

"What is this sun that you all speak of? Do you mean anything by the word?"

"Yes, we jolly well do," said Scrubb.

"Can you tell me what it's like?" asked the Witch (thrum, thrum, thrum, went the strings).

"Please it your Grace," said the Prince, very coldly and politely. "You see that lamp. It is round and yellow and gives light to the whole room; and hangeth moreover from the roof. Now that thing which we call the sun is like the lamp, only far greater and brighter. It giveth light to the whole Overworld and hangeth in the sky."

"Hangeth from what, my lord?" asked the Witch; and then, while they were all still thinking how to answer her, she added, with another of her soft, silver laughs: "You see? When you try to think out clearly what this sun must be, you cannot tell me. You can only tell me it is like the lamp. Your sun is a dream; and there is nothing in that dream that was not copied from the lamp. The lamp is the real thing; the sun is but a tale, a children's story."

"Yes, I see now," said Jill in a heavy, hopeless tone. "It must be so." And while she said this, it seemed to her to be very good sense.

Slowly and gravely the Witch repeated, "There is no sun." And they all said nothing. She repeated in a softer and deeper voice, "There is no sun." After a pause, and after a struggle in their minds, all four of them said together, "You are right. There is no sun." It was such a relief to give in and say it.

"There never was a sun," said the Witch.

"No. There never was a sun," said the Prince, and the Marsh-wiggle, and the children.

For the last few minutes Jill had been feeling that there was something she must remember at all costs. And now she did. But it was dreadfully hard to say it. She felt as if huge weights were laid on her lips. At last, with an effort that seemed to take all the good out of her, she said:

"There's Aslan."

"Aslan?" said the Witch, quickening ever so slightly the pace of her thrumming. "What a pretty name! What does it mean?"

"He is the great Lion who called us out of our own world," said Scrubb, "and sent us into this to find Prince Rilian."

"What is a lion?" asked the Witch.

"Oh, hang it all!" said Scrubb. "Don't you know? How can we describe it to her? Have you ever seen a cat?"

"Surely," said the Queen. "I love cats."

"Well, a lion is a little bit—only a little bit mind you,— like a huge cat—with a mane. At least, it's not like a horse's mane, you know, it's more like a judge's wig. And it's yellow. And terrifically strong."

The Witch shook her head. "I see," she said, "that we should do no better with your lion, as you call it, than we did with your sun. You have seen lamps, and so you imagined a bigger and better lamp and called it the sun. You've seen cats, and now you want a bigger and better cat, and it's to be called a lion. Well, 'tis a pretty make-believe, though, to say truth, it would suit you all better if you were younger. And look how you can put nothing into your make-believe without copying it from the real world, this world of mine, which is the only world. But even you children are too old for such play. As for you, my Lord Prince, that art a man full grown, fie upon you! Are you not ashamed of such toys? Come, all of you. Put away these childish tricks. I have work for you all in the real world. There is no Narnia, no Overworld, no sky, no sun, no Aslan. And now, to bed all. And let us begin a wiser life tomorrow. But, first, to bed; to sleep; deep sleep, soft pillows, sleep without foolish dreams."

The Prince and the two children were standing with their heads hung down, their cheeks flushed, their eyes half-closed; the strength all gone from them; the enchantment almost complete. But Puddleglum, desperately gathering all his strength, walked over to the fire. Then he did a very brave thing. He knew it wouldn't hurt him quite as much as it would hurt a human; for his feet (which were bare) were webbed and hard and cold-blooded like a duck's. But he knew it would hurt him badly enough; and so it did. With his bare foot he stamped on the fire, grinding a large part of it into ashes on the flat hearth. And three things happened at once.

First, the sweet heavy smell grew very much less. For

though the whole fire had not been put out, a good bit of it had, and what remained smelled very largely of burnt Marsh-wiggle, which is not at all an enchanting smell. This instantly made everyone's brain far clearer. The Prince and the children held up their heads again and opened their eyes.

Secondly, the Witch, in a loud, terrible voice, utterly different from all the sweet tones she had been using up till now, called out, "What are you doing? Dare to touch my fire again, mud-filth, and I'll turn the blood to fire inside your veins."

Thirdly, the pain itself made Puddleglum's head for a moment perfectly clear and he knew exactly what he really thought. There is nothing like a good shock of pain for dissolving certain kinds of magic.

"One word, Ma'am," he said, coming back from the fire, limping, because of the pain. "One word. All you've been saying is quite right, I shouldn't wonder. I'm a chap who always likes to know the worst and then put the best face I can on it. So I won't deny any of what you said. But there's one thing more to be said, even so. Suppose we have only dreamed, or made up, all those things—trees and grass and sun and moon and stars and Aslan himself. Suppose we have. Then all I can say is that, in that case, the made-up things seem a good deal more important than the real ones. Suppose this black pit of a kingdom of yours is the only world. Well, it strikes me as a pretty poor one. And that's a funny thing, when you come to think of it. We're just babies making up a game, if you're right. But four babies playing a game can make a play-world which licks your real world hollow. That's why I'm going to stand by the play-world. I'm on Aslan's side even if there isn't any Aslan to lead it I'm going to live as like a Narnian as I can even if there isn't any Narnia. So, thanking you kindly for our supper, if these two gentlemen and the young lady are ready, we're leaving your court at once and setting out in the dark to spend our lives looking for Overland. Not that our lives will be very long, I should think; but that's small loss if the world's as dull a place as you say."

"Oh, hurrah! Good old Puddleglum!" cried Scrubb and Jill. But the Prince shouted suddenly, "Ware! Look to the Witch."

When they did look their hair nearly stood on end.

The instrument dropped from her hands. Her arms appeared to be fastened to her sides. Her legs were intertwined with each other, and her feet disappeared. The long green train of her skirt thickened and grew solid, and seemed to be all one piece with the writhing green pillar of her interlocked legs. And that writhing green pillar was curving and swaying as if it had no joints, or else were all joints. Her head was thrown far back and while her nose grew longer and longer, every other part of her face seemed to disappear, except her eyes. Huge flaming eyes they were now, without brows or lashes. All this takes time to write down; it happened so quickly that there was only just time to see it. Long before there was time to do anything, the change was complete, and the great serpent which the Witch had become, green as poison, thick as Jill's waist, had flung two or three coils of its loathsome body round the Prince's legs. Quick as lightning another great loop darted round, intending to pinion his sword-arm to his side. But the Prince was just in time. He raised his arms and got them clear: the living knot closed only round his chest—ready to crack his ribs like firewood when it drew tight.

The Prince caught the creature's neck in his left hand, trying to squeeze it till it choked. This held its face (if you could call it a face) about five inches from his own. The forked tongue flickered horribly in and out, but could not reach him. With his right hand he drew back his sword for the strongest blow he could give. Meanwhile Scrubb and Puddleglum had drawn their weapons and rushed to his aid. All three blows fell at once: Scrubb's (which did not even pierce the scales and did no good) on the body of the snake below the Prince's hand, but the Prince's own blow and Puddleglum's both on its neck. Even that did not quite kill it, though it began to loosen its hold on Rilian's legs and chest. With repeated blows they hacked off its head. The horrible thing went on coiling and moving like a bit of wire long after it had died; and the floor, as you may imagine, was a nasty mess.

The Prince, when he had breath, said, "Gentlemen, I thank you." Then the three conquerors stood staring at one another and panting, without another word, for a long time. Jill had very wisely sat down and was keeping quiet; she was saying to herself, "I hope I don't faint—or blub—or do anything idiotic."

"My royal mother is avenged," said Rilian presently. "This is undoubtedly the same worm that I pursued in vain by the fountain in the forest of Narnia, so many years ago. All these years I have been the slave of my mother's slayer. Yet I am glad, gentlemen, that the foul Witch took to her serpent form at the last. It would not have suited well either with my heart or with my honour to have slain a woman. But look to the lady." He meant Jill.

"I'm all right, thanks," said she.

"Damsel," said the Prince, bowing to her. "You are of a high courage, and therefore, I doubt not, you come of a

noble blood in your own world. But come, friends. Here is some wine left. Let us refresh ourselves and each pledge his fellows. After that, to our plans."

"A jolly good idea," said Scrubb.

The Hand of Glory

RICHARD HARRIS BARHAM

Three thieves consult a witch to help them in their evil doings by preparing a Hand of Glory. Belief in the Hand of Glory was a wide-spread superstition. It was thought that the hand of a hanged man had the power to open doors and to put people to sleep; everything, in fact, that the well-equipped burglar needed. At the end of the story justice is done to everyone, witch included.

Although he has written some splendidly blood-curdling lines, Barham's approach is light-hearted. This poem comes from The Ingoldsby Legends. *The fame of one of the legends,* The Jackdaw of Rheims, *has overshadowed the others. Many of them are marked by the same high spirits and ingenuity of the verse.*

This version of The Hand of Glory *has been shortened to concentrate on the essential narrative. Like many comic writers Barham uses references to happenings in his own time, which are not always easy for later readers to understand.*

On the lone bleak moor, at the midnight hour,
Beneath the Gallows Tree,
   Hand in hand the Murderers stand
By one, by two, by three!
   And the Moon that night with a grey, cold light
Each baleful object tips;
   One half of her form is seen through the storm,
And the other half's hid in Eclipse!
   And the cold Wind howls, and the Thunder growls,
And the Lightning is broad and bright;

And altogether it's very bad weather,
And an unpleasant sort of a Night!
   "Now mount who list, and close by the wrist
Sever me quickly the Dead Man's fist!—
   Now climb who dare where he swings in air,
And pluck me five locks of the Dead Man's hair!"

There's an old woman dwells upon Tappington Moor,
She hath years on her back at least the threescore,
And some people fancy a great many more;
   Her nose it is hook'd, her back it is crook'd,
   Her eyes blear and red: on the top of her head
   Is a mutch,[1] and on that a shocking bad hat,
Extinguisher-shaped, the brim narrow and flat!
Then,—My Gracious!—her beard!—it would sadly
      perplex
A spectator at first to distinguish her sex;
Nor, I'll venture to say, without scrutiny cou'd he
Pronounce her, off-handed, a Punch or a Judy.
Did you see her, in short, that mud-hovel within,
With her knees to her nose, and her nose to her chin,

[1] cap or coif.

Leering up with that queer, indescribable grin,
You'd lift up your hands in amazement, and cry,
"—Well!—I never did see such a regular *Guy*!"

    And now before that Old Woman's door,
    Where nought that's good may be,
      Hand in hand the Murderers stand
    By one, by two, by three!
Oh! 'tis a horrible sight to view,
In that horrible hovel, that horrible crew,
By the pale blue glare of that flickering flame,
Doing the deed that hath never a name!
    'Tis awful to hear those words of fear!

The pray'r muttered backwards, and said with a sneer!
(Matthew Hopkins himself has assured us that when
A Witch says her prayers, she begins with Amen.)—
    'Tis awful to see on that Old Woman's knee
The dead shrivell'd hand, as she clasps it with glee!
    And now with care, the five locks of hair
From the skull of the Gentleman dangling up there,
    With the grease and the fat of a black Tom Cat
    She hastens to mix, and to twist into wicks,
And one on the thumb and each finger to fix—

    "Now open lock to the Dead Man's knock!
    Fly bolt, and bar, and band!—
    Nor move, nor swerve, joint, muscle, or nerve,
At the spell of the Dead Man's hand!
Sleep all who sleep!—Wake all who wake!—
But be as the Dead for the Dead Man's sake!"

All is silent! all is still,
Save the ceaseless moan of the bubbling rill
As it wells from the bosom of Tappington Hill,
   And in Tappington Hall great and small,
Gentle and Simple, Squire and Groom,
Each one hath sought his separate room,
And Sleep her dun mantle hath o'er them cast,
For the midnight hour hath long been past!

All is darksome in earth and sky,
Save, from yon casement, narrow and high,
   A quivering beam on the tiny stream
Plays, like some taper's fitful gleam
By one that is watching wearily.

Within that casement, narrow and high,
In his secret lair, where none may spy,
Sits one whose brow is wrinkled with care,
And the thin grey locks of his falling hair
Have left his bald little pate all bare;
    For his full-bottom'd wig hangs, bushy and big
On the top of his old-fashioned, high-backed chair.
—And there by many a sparkling heap
    Of the good red gold, the tale is told
What powerful spell avails to keep
That care-worn man from his needful sleep!

Haply, he deems no eye can see
As he gloats on his treasure greedily,—
    The shining store of glittering ore,
The fair rose noble, the bright moidore,
But there's one that watches as well as he:
    For, wakeful and sly, in a closet hard by,
On a truckle-bed lieth a little Foot-page,
A boy who's uncommonly sharp for his age,
And while that old Gentleman's counting his hoards,
Little Hugh peeps through a crack in the boards!

    There's a voice in the air, there's a step on the stair,
The old man starts in his cane-backed chair;
    Then half arose from beside his toes
His little pug-dog with his little pug-nose,
    For low, yet clear, now fall on the ear,
—Where once pronounced for ever they dwell—
The unholy words of the Dead Man's spell!
    "Open lock to the Dead Man's knock!

Fly bolt, and bar, and band!
    Nor move, nor swerve, joint, muscle, or nerve,
At the spell of the Dead Man's hand!
Sleep all who sleep!—Wake all who wake!—
But be as the Dead for the Dead Man's sake!"

Nor lock, nor bolt, nor bar avails,
Nor stout oak panel thick-studded with nails.
Heavy and harsh the hinges creak,
Though they had been oil'd in the course of the week
The door opens wide as wide may be,
    And there they stand, that murderous band,
    Led by the light of the *Glorious Hand,*
        By one!—by two!—by three!
They have passed through the porch, they have passed
        through the hall,
Where the Porter sat snoring against the wall;
    And now they are there, on the head of the stair,
—I really don't think any money would bribe
Me the horrible scene that ensued to describe,
    Or the wild, wild, glare of that old man's eye,
    His dumb despair and deep agony.
But, oh! what a thing 'tis to see and to know
That the bare knife is raised in the hand of the foe,
Without hope to repel or to ward off the blow!—
—Enough!—let's pass over as fast as we can
The fate of that grey, that unhappy old man!

    But fancy poor Hugh, aghast at the view,
    Powerless alike to speak or to do!
'Tis lucky for him that the chink in the wall
He has peep'd through so long, is narrow and small!

'Tis early dawn—the morn is grey,
And the clouds and the tempest have pass'd away,
And all things betoken a very fine day;
But, while the lark her carol is singing,
Shrieks and screams are through Tappington ringing!
Gentle or Simple, Squire or Groom,
All seek at once that old Gentleman's room;
   And there, on the floor, drenched in its gore
A ghastly corpse lies exposed to the view,
Carotid and jugular both cut through;
   And there, by its side, 'mid the crimson tide,
Kneels a little Foot-page of tenderest years;
Adown his pale cheeks the fast-falling tears
Are coursing each other round and big,
And he's staunching the blood with a full-bottomed wig!
Alas! and alack for his staunching!—'tis plain,
As anatomists tell us, that never again
Shall life revisit the foully slain,
When once they've been cut through the jugular vein.

There's a hue and cry through the county of Kent,
And in chase of the cut-throats a Constable's sent,
But no one can tell the man which way they went:
There's a little Foot-page with that Constable goes,
And a little pug-dog with a little pug-nose.

   In Rochester town, at the sign of the Crown,
Three shabby-genteel men are just sitting down
To a fat stubble-goose with potatoes done brown;
   When a little Foot-page rushes in, in a rage,
Upsetting the apple-sauce, onions, and sage.
That little Foot-page takes the first by the throat,

And a little pug-dog takes the next by the coat,
And a Constable seizes the one more remote;
And fair rose-nobles and broad moidores,
The Waiter pulls out of their pockets by scores,
And the Boots and the Chambermaids run in and stare;
And the Constable says, with a dignified air,
"You're *wanted*, Gen'lemen, one and all,
For that 'ere precious lark at Tappington Hall!"

There's a black gibbet frowns upon Tappington Moor,
Where a former black gibbet has frowned before:
    It is as black as black may be,
        And murderers there are dangling in air,
    By one!—by two!—by three!

There's a horrid old hag in a steeple-crowned hat,
Round her neck they have tied to a hempen cravat
A Dead Man's hand, and a dead Tom Cat!
They have tied up her thumbs, they have tied up her toes,
    They have tied up her eyes, they have tied up her limbs;
Into Tappington mill-dam souse she goes,
    With a whoop and a halloo! "She swims!—She swims!"
        They have dragged her to land, and everyone's hand
    Is grasping a faggot, a billet, or brand,
When a queer-looking horseman, drest all in black,
Snatches up that old harridan just like a sack
To the crupper behind him, puts spurs to his hack,
Makes a dash through the crowd, and is off in a crack!
    No one can tell, though they guess pretty well,
Which way that grim rider and old woman go,
For all see he's a sort of infernal Ducrow;
And she scream'd so, and cried, we may fairly decide
That the old woman did not much relish her ride!

MORAL

The truest of stories confirms beyond doubt
That truest of adages—"Murder will out!"
In vain may the blood-spiller "double" and fly,
In vain even witchcraft and sorcery try;
Although for a time he may 'scape, by-and-by
He'll be sure to be caught by a Hugh and a Cry.

Witches' Sabbats

The idea of the "witches' sabbat"—a meeting of all the witches in a particular district—has made a great appeal to people's imaginations. We have many descriptions of these meetings, but there is still argument as to what happened at them. Some modern writers say that the descriptions of sabbats are hysterical nonsense, the result of enforced confessions. Others say that the sabbat is the remains of ancient religious rites, perhaps going back to the Stone Age. Here are four views of a witches' sabbat. This particular spelling has been in use since the seventeenth century, and is convenient for distinguishing between the witches' festival and the Jewish and Christian use of the word.

ITALY

This account comes from the Compendium Maleficarum *(Handbook of Witches) by the seventeenth-century Italian friar, Francesco-Maria Guazzo.*

When these members of the devil have met together, they generally light a foul and horrid fire. The devil is president of the assembly and sits on a throne, in some terrible shape, as of a goat or a dog, and they approach him to adore him. . . .

There are tables placed and drawn up, and they sit and start to eat of the food which the demon has provided, or which they have themselves brought. But all who have sat down to such tables confess that the feasts are all foul either in appearance or in smell, so that they would easily nauseate the most hungry stomach. . . . They say that there is plenty of everything except bread and salt.

SWEDEN

This account of the extraordinary happenings alleged to have taken place at Mora in 1669 comes from Satan's Invisible World *by George Sinclair. This book was published in Edinburgh in 1685 and went through many editions. It helped to keep a belief in witchcraft alive in Scotland, long after it had died in England.*

We of the Province of Elfdale do confess that we used to go to a Gravel-pit which lays hard by a Cross-way, and there we put on a Vest over our heads, and then danced round, and after this ran to the Cross-way, and called the Devil thrice, first with a still Voice: the second time somewhat louder: and the third time very loud, with these words, Antecessor come and carry us to Blockula. Whereupon immediately he used to appear, but in different Habits, but for the most part we saw him in a Grey-Coat and red and blue Stockings. He had a red beard, a high crowned Hat, with linen of diverse colours wrapt about it, and long Garters upon his Stockings. . . .

Then he asked us whether we would serve him with Soul and Body? If we were content to do so, he set us on a Beast, which he had there ready, and carried us over Churches and High Walls: and after all, we came to a Green-meadow, where Blockula lies. . . .

They unanimously confessed that Blockula is Situated in a large Meadow, like a Plain Sea, wherein you see no end. The Place or House they met at had before it a great Gate painted with many diverse colours on it; through this

Gate they went into a little Meadow distant from the other where the beasts went, which they used to ride on. . . .

In a huge large Room of the House, they said, there stood a very large long Table at which the Witches did sit down. And that hard by this Room was another Chamber, where there were some lovely and delicate beds.

The first thing they said they must do at Blockula was, That they must deny all and devote themselves Body and Soul to the Devil, and promise to serve him Faithfully, and confirm it with an Oath. Hereupon they cut their fingers and writ their Names in his Book. . . .

After this they sat down to Table, and those that the Devil esteemed most were placed nearest to him; but the Children must stand at the Door, where he himself gives them meat and drink. . . .

LANCASHIRE—FICTION

Here is a witches' sabbat, as seen by a well-known nineteenth-century novelist Harrison Ainsworth, in The Lancashire Witches. *The Lancashire witches were real people who were tried for witchcraft in 1612. By the time Ainsworth was writing, witchcraft seemed merely a folly of past ages, and so he could treat the subject in an imaginative way.*

"Whither are you going?" cried Alizon.

"To the moon! to the stars! anywhere!" rejoined Dorothy with a laugh of frantic glee.

"I will go with you," cried Alizon, echoing the laugh.

"Here and there—here and there!" exclaimed Dorothy, taking her hand. *"Emen hetan! Emen hetan!"*

As the mystic words were uttered, they started away. It

seemed as if no impediments could stop them. How they crossed the closet, passed through a sliding panel into the abbot's room, entered the oratory, and from it descended a secret staircase to the garden, they knew not; but there they were, gliding swiftly along in the moonlight, like winged spirits.

What took them towards the conventual church they could not say; but they were drawn thither . . . irresistibly.

Nothing surprised them then, or they might have been struck by the dense vapour enveloping the monastic ruins, and shrouding them from view; nor was it until they entered the desecrated fabric that any consciousness of what was passing around returned to them.

Their ears were then assailed by a wild hubbub of discordant sounds—hootings and croakings as of owls and ravens, shrieks and jarring cries as of night-birds, bellowings as of cattle, groans and dismal sounds, mixed with unearthly laughter.

Undefined and extraordinary shapes, whether men or women, beings of this world or of another, they could not tell, though they judged them the latter, flew past with wild whoops and piercing cries, flapping the air, as if with great leathern, batlike wings, or bestriding black, monstrous, misshapen steeds.

Fantastical and grotesque were these objects, yet hideous and appalling. Now and then a red and fiery star would whiz crackling through the air, and then exploding, break into numerous pale, phosphoric lights, that danced awhile overhead, and then flitted away among the ruins.

The ground seemed to heave and tremble beneath the footsteps, as if the graves were opening to give forth their dead, while toads and hissing reptiles crept forth.

✳

They moved slowly towards the transept, taking care to keep under the shelter of the columns.

On reaching the last pillar, behind which they remained, an extraordinary and fearful spectacle burst upon them. A large fire was burning in the midst of the choir, the smoke of which, ascending in eddying wreaths, formed a dark canopy overhead, where it was mixed with the steam issuing from a large, black, bubbling cauldron set on the blazing embers.

Around the fire were ranged, in a wide circle, an assemblage of men and women, but chiefly the latter, and of these almost all old, hideous, and of malignant aspect, their grim and malignant features looking ghastly in the lurid light.

Above them, amid the smoke and steam, wheeled bat and flittermouse, horned owl and screech-owl in mazy circles. The weird assemblage chattered together in some wild jargon, mumbling and muttering spells and incantations, chanting fearfully with hoarse, cracked voices as in a wild chorus, and anon breaking into a loud and long-continued peal of laughter.

LANCASHIRE—?

Finally, here are the Lancashire witches again. This is how Thomas Potts described them in The Wonderful Discovery of Witches in the County of Lancaster, *which was published in 1613. Here he writes of a meeting at Malking Tower, where there was "great cheer, merry company, and much conference." "The persons aforesaid had to their dinner, beef, bacon, and roasted mutton." This meeting has been called "the first*

English sabbat", but it does not bear much resemblance to the other sabbats described.

James Device's Confession.

And being examined, he further said, that upon Sheare-Thursday last, in the evening, he stole a Wether[1] from John Robinson of Barley and brought it to his Grandmother's house, Old Demdike, and there killed it: and that upon the day following, being Good-Friday, about twelve of the clock in the daytime, there dined in his house a number of persons, whereof three were men and the rest women; and they met there for three Causes.

1. The first was for the naming of the Spirit which Alizon Device, now prisoner at Lancaster, had, but did not name him because she was not there.

2. The second Cause was for the delivery of his said Grandmother; his said sister Alizon; Anne Chattox and her daughter Redferne; killing the Gaoler at Lancaster; and before the next Assizes to blow up the Castle there, to the end aforesaid persons might by that means make an escape and get away.

3. And the third Cause was for that there was a woman dwelling in Gisborne Parish, who came into his Grandmother's house and craved assistance of the rest of them that were there then, for the killing of Master Lister of Westby, because (as she then said) he had born malice unto her, and had thought to have her put away at the last Assizes at York, but could not. And he heard the said woman say, That her power was not strong enough to do it herself, being now less than before time it hath been.

[1] Ram.

Rapunzel

JAKOB and WILHELM GRIMM told by ANDREW LANG

There are several famous children's books which were not written for children at all in the first place, such as Gulliver's Travels *and* Robinson Crusoe. *Another is the collection of German folk tales made by two brothers called Jakob and Wilhelm Grimm. Jakob is also famous as one of the first people to study how languages have developed, but most people know him chiefly for his share in* Grimms' Fairy Tales. *These were first published in England during the 1820's with illustrations by George Cruikshank, and they have been popular as a children's book ever since.*

Rapunzel is a tale of a witch and a beautiful girl with long hair. This version comes from The Red Fairy Book *by Andrew Lang. Lang wrote twelve of these "colour" fairy books and used stories from all over the world. He often had to point out, "I do not write the stories out of my own head".*

ONCE upon a time a man and his wife were very unhappy because they had no children. These good people had a little window at the back of their house, which looked into the most lovely garden, full of all manner of beautiful flowers and vegetables; but the garden was surrounded by a high wall, and no one dared to enter it for it belonged to a witch of great power who was feared by the whole world. One day the woman stood at the window overlooking the garden and saw there a bed full of the finest rampion. The leaves looked so fresh and green that she longed to eat them. The desire grew day by day, and just because she knew she couldn't possibly get any, she pined away and became pale and wretched. Then her husband grew alarmed and said:

"What ails you, dear wife?"

"Oh," she answered, "if I don't get some rampion to eat out of the garden behind the house, I know I shall die."

The man, who loved her dearly, said to himself, "Come! Rather than let your wife die you shall fetch her some rampion, no matter the cost." So at dusk he climbed over the wall to the witch's garden and, hastily gathering a handful of rampion leaves, he returned with them to his wife. She made them into a salad, which tasted so good that her longing for the forbidden food was greater than ever. If she were to know any peace of mind, there was nothing for it but that her husband should climb over the garden wall again and fetch her some more. So at dusk over he went, but when he reached the other side he drew back in terror, for there, standing before him, was the old witch.

"How dare you," she said, with a wrathful glance, "climb into my garden and steal my rampion like a common thief? You shall suffer for your foolhardiness."

"Oh," he implored, "pardon my presumption; necessity alone drove me to the deed. My wife saw your rampion from her window and had such a desire for it that she certainly would have died if her wish had not been gratified."

Then the witch's anger was a little appeased, and she said,

"If it's as you say, you may take as much rampion away with you as you like, but on one condition only—that you give me the child your wife will shortly bring into the world. All shall go well with it and I will look after it like a mother."

The man in his terror agreed to everything she asked. As soon as the child was born the witch appeared and, having given it the name of Rapunzel, which is the same as rampion, she carried it off with her.

Rapunzel was the most beautiful child under the sun. When she was twelve years old the witch shut her up in a tower, in the middle of a great wood, and the tower had neither stairs nor doors, only high up at the very top a small window. When the old witch wanted to get in she stood underneath and called out:

> "Rapunzel, Rapunzel,
> Let down your golden hair."

For Rapunzel had wonderful long hair, and it was as fine as spun gold. Whenever she heard the witch's voice she unloosed her plaits, and let her hair fall down out of the window, and the old witch climbed up by it.

After they had lived like this for a few years, it happened one day that a prince was riding through the wood and passed by the tower. As he drew near it he heard someone singing so sweetly that he stood spellbound and listened. It was Rapunzel in her loneliness trying to while away the time by letting her sweet voice ring out into the wood. The prince longed to see the owner of the voice, but he sought in vain for a door in the tower. He rode home, but he was so haunted by the song he had heard that he returned every day to the wood and listened. One day, when he was standing thus behind a tree, he saw the old witch approach and heard her call out:

> "Rapunzel, Rapunzel,
> Let down your golden hair."

Then Rapunzel let down her plaits and the witch climbed up by them.

"So that's the staircase, is it?" said the prince. "Then I too will climb it and try my luck."

So on the following day, at dusk, he went to the foot of the tower and cried:

> "Rapunzel, Rapunzel,
> Let down your golden hair."

And as soon as she had let it down the prince climbed up.

At first Rapunzel was terribly frightened when a man came in, for she had never seen one before. But the prince spoke to her kindly and told her at once that his heart had been so touched by her singing he felt he should know no peace of mind till he had seen her. Very soon Rapunzel forgot her fear, and when he asked her to marry him she consented at once.

For, she thought, he is young and handsome, and I'll certainly be happier with him than with the old witch. So she put her hand in his and said:

"Yes, I will gladly go with you, only how am I to get down out of the tower? Every time you come to see me you must bring a skein of silk with you, and I will make a ladder of them, and when it is finished I will climb down by it, and you will take me away on your horse."

They arranged that, till the ladder was ready, he was to come to her every evening, because the old woman was with her during the day. The old witch, of course, knew nothing of what was going on, till one day Rapunzel, not thinking of what she was about, turned to the witch and said: "How is it, good mother, that you are so much harder to pull up than the young prince? He is always with me in a moment."

"Oh, you wicked child," cried the witch. "What is this I hear? I thought I had hidden you safely from the whole world and in spite of it you have managed to deceive me."

In her wrath she seized Rapunzel's beautiful hair, wound it round and round her left hand, and then grasping a pair of scissors in her right, snip snap, off it came, and the beautiful plaits lay on the ground. And, worse than this, she was so hard-hearted that she took Rapunzel to a lonely desert place and left her there to dwell in loneliness and misery.

But on the evening of the day in which she had driven poor Rapunzel away, the witch fastened the plaits on to a hook in the window, and when the prince came and called out:

"Rapunzel, Rapunzel,
Let down your golden hair,"

she let them down, and the prince climbed up as usual. But instead of his beloved Rapunzel he found the old witch, who fixed her evil, glittering eyes on him, and cried mockingly:

"Ah, ah! You thought to find your lady love, but the pretty bird has flown and its song is dumb. The cat caught it and will scratch out your eyes too. Rapunzel is lost to you for ever—you will never see her more."

The prince was beside himself with grief, and in his despair he jumped right down from the tower and, though he escaped with his life, the thorns among which he fell pierced his eyes. Then he wandered, blind and miserable, through the wood, eating nothing but roots and berries and weeping and lamenting the loss of his lovely bride.

So he wandered about for some years, as wretched and

unhappy as he could well be, and at last he came to the desert place where Rapunzel was living. Of a sudden he heard a voice which seemed strangely familiar to him. He walked eagerly in the direction of the sound, and when he was quite close, Rapunzel recognized him and fell on his neck and wept. Two of her tears touched his eyes, and in a moment they became quite clear again, and he saw as well as ever he had. Then he led her to his kingdom, where they lived happily ever after.

A Quiet Night

FOR A PEACEFUL NIGHT

EDMUND SPENSER

In thinking about the past, we need to remind ourselves how dark it was at night, when the only light was the moon. Darkness could breed fears, including a fear of witches.

When the sixteenth-century Book of Common Prayer says, "Lighten our darkness, we beseech thee, O Lord; and by thy great mercy defend us from all perils and dangers of this night", it is a very urgent and real plea. Two great writers of the same time take up the theme.

The strange title of Spenser's poem, Epithalamion, simply means wedding-song. In the sixteenth century, people all over Europe were passionately interested in classical literature, so it would have seemed natural for Spenser to use a word that came originally from Greek. He wrote the poem as a wedding present for his wife at the time of their marriage in 1594. Few wedding presents can ever have lasted as long. In this verse he speaks of the many creatures that could disturb the night: Puck, witches, hobgoblins, ghosts, and asks that they should be quiet and still.

In Hamlet Shakespeare mentions another belief, that at Christmas the cock crows all night, and witches and fairies are powerless.

Let no lamenting cries, nor doleful tears
Be heard all night within, nor yet without:
Ne¹ let false whispers, breeding hidden fears,
Break gentle sleep with misconceivèd doubt.

¹ Not, or nor.

Let no deluding dreams, nor dreadful sights,
Make sudden sad affrights;
Ne let house-fires, nor lightning's helpless harm
Ne let the Puck, nor other evil sprights,
Ne let mischievous witches with their charms,
Ne let hobgoblins, names whose sense we see not,
Fray us with things that be not:
Let not the screetch owl nor the stork be heard,
Nor the night raven that still deadly yells:
Nor damned ghosts, called up with mighty spells,
Nor grisly vultures, make us once affeared:
Ne the let unpleasant choir of frogs still croaking
Make us to wish their choking.
Let none of these their dreary accents sing:
Ne let the woods them answer, nor their echoes ring.

AT CHRISTMAS

WILLIAM SHAKESPEARE

Some say that ever 'gainst that season comes
Wherein our Saviour's birth is celebrated,
The bird of dawning singeth all day long;
And then, they say, no spirit can walk abroad;
The nights are wholesome; then no planets strike,
No fairy takes,[1] nor witch hath power to charm,
So hallowed and so gracious is the time.

[1] Strikes with disease.

The Great-Aunt

ARTHUR RANSOME

The Great-aunt was ruining everyone's holiday. Nancy and Peggy Blackett, the "Amazon pirates", wanted to go and camp with John, Susan, Titty, and Roger, the crew of the ship Swallow. *But their Great-aunt had come to stay. She insisted that they should stay at home, wear their best clothes, practise the piano, and never be late for meals. Worst of all, she was so unpleasant that she had made their mother cry. Titty, the Swallows' able-seaman, decided that it was time to do something about this. So Titty became a witch.*

In this perceptive study, taken from Swallowdale, *Arthur Ransome shows the effect of black magic, not on the intended victim, but on the "witch" herself.*

WHEN the camp was itself again, with the tents up and the parrot cage once more on its stone pedestal, and they were watching Roger carefully tightening his guy-ropes, Titty asked Nancy, "Has the great-aunt been getting worse? Is that why you want to wall her up? But it ought to be in a new bridge or a castle or something like that. It would be waste to do it with a cave."

"Anything would be too good for her," said Nancy. "It isn't as if it was only us. We can stand it. But she *will* go for mother. There was an awful row again just because we ran into a calm the day we helped you to move camp. And, anyway, who can help being late in summer? But the moment she looks at her watch and thinks there ought to be a meal she doesn't wait decently till the gong's been banged once or twice in the house and then taken out in the garden and banged good and proper in case we're up on the fell. She just goes into the dining-room and waits. And ten to one cook isn't ready. And the old gong doesn't go till she is. And mother doesn't know what to do between the great-aunt and poor old cook. And even when her food's shoved under her nose the great-aunt won't begin until we've been rounded up. And when Uncle Jim isn't there she's even worse. Last night she made mother cry."

Titty stared and her mouth stayed open,

"It was about us, of course. She dragged father in. We knew because after we'd gone to bed we couldn't help hearing Uncle Jim talking to mother just outside our window, and he said, 'Bob would have liked them just as they are.' And he called mother 'Mops,' which he only does sometimes. Then we made a noise and mother said, 'Go to sleep, you donkeys,' and pretended to laugh. But she couldn't."

Nancy walked suddenly away, but she came back in a moment with her face very red.

"If only we could get the G.A. to go," she said. "I thought of putting little stones in her bed in between the mattress and the sheet. And Peggy thought of putting. drops of cod-liver oil in her morning tea. But it's no good. It would only be worse for mother."

"In some places," said Titty, "the natives do this sort of thing when they have an enemy. I found it in a book. They make a doll and call it the name of the person. Then they stick pins in it, and every pin they stick in the doll is felt by the person, and if they stick the pins right through, the person dies. You could do that, and stick the pins in just a little way every night until she was so uncomfortable she would go of her own accord."

Nancy laughed bitterly. "You could fill a doll cramfull of pins. You could use it as a pin-cushion and it wouldn't hurt the great-aunt. She wouldn't notice it. Pins would blunt on her."

"Perhaps they ought to be silver," said Titty. "It said in the same book about shooting witches and were-wolves. They always had to use a silver bullet."

"Susan's pins look like silver ones," said Roger, who was listening now that his tent was properly pitched.

"They might do," said Titty. "How could the great-aunt find out that they weren't really silver? She couldn't see you sticking the pins in."

"All that's rubbish," said Susan. "Nobody believes in it now."

"It must have worked or people wouldn't have gone on doing it," said Titty.

"Anyway it's a bad sort of magic," said Susan.

"But it would be good magic if it would make the great-aunt go away and stop being beastly to Mrs Blackett."

"Well, nobody's going to try it," said Susan.

"She'll go sooner or later," said Nancy. "She doesn't usually stay more than a week. I believe she's only stopping now because she knows mother would let us come and camp with you if she wasn't here."

Nancy and Peggy were already hurrying down Swallow-dale to go through the woods to the road that would take them along the shore of the lake back to Beckfoot and to all kinds of trouble. They went off at such a pace that the others had hard work to keep up with them.

As soon as they were all out of Swallowdale, Titty went straight to Peter Duck's cave. She found it in darkness. The candle was out. She got out a box of matches from her tent and went into the cave again. Yes, she had been quite right. The lantern had got very hot and had melted the candle too fast, and all round it on the ledge of rock that made a shelf was a mass of thick white candle-grease.

"It isn't wax," she said to herself, "but it's good enough for the great-aunt. Anyway, it'll have to do."

It was not that Able-seaman Titty knew very much of the mother of the Amazons. She had seen her only twice, once last year after the great storm on Wild Cat Island, when she had been full of chatter and jollity, and once this year sitting sadly in the carriage side by side with the great-aunt, while Nancy and Peggy sat on the other seat facing them, and looking not at all like pirates. It was not really of Mrs Blackett she was thinking. She was thinking of her own mother. When Nancy told of how the great-aunt had made Mrs Blackett cry, Titty thought of what she would do if someone were to do that to mother, and in a moment she was feeling as if the great-aunt had made mother cry, so that there was nothing Titty would not have been ready to do to the great-aunt if only it would stop her. She did not know if the wax image would work, but it was worth trying, even with candle-grease, because there was nothing else that she could do.

She picked up the little lantern from the shelf of rock and the candle-grease that had oozed out and hardened all round it came away like a thick whitish plate stuck to the bottom of the lantern. Her match went out. But a little light came through the doorway, and after waiting a minute till her eyes had grown accustomed to the dark, she stooped low, and carefully shielding the lantern for fear of knocking it on something, she came out with the slab of candle-grease unbroken.

Outside in Swallowdale, sitting by the fire with the

sticks crackling cheerfully, the clean blue smoke climbing up into the evening sky, and the parrot out of his cage and preening his breast feathers, she very nearly gave the thing up. Looking at the smooth, hard, oily slab of candle-grease which she had now broken off the lantern, she began to doubt if she could do it. What was the great-aunt like? She remembered the stiff, upright figure in the carriage, but could not see her face, try as she would. Then she remembered the native images she had seen in a museum. After all, they weren't very much like anything.

"It's the name that matters," she said to herself, "and the magic."

The name would be easy. She would simply call the thing "great-aunt". The magic would be more difficult. Just making a candle-grease doll and calling it "great-aunt" would hardly be enough. There would have to be a spell. Why, of course she knew the way to do it. She remembered the African and Jamaican stories told by her mother in the evenings, and how when the king's wife died in the heat of the weather and the king he was real vexed, he sent for the Obeah woman who was the witch and had wrinkles deep as ditches on her brown face and told her to cast a spell so that nobody should use the queen's name again, because his queen she was so beautiful. "And de Obeah woman, dat was de witch, she walk roun' de room an' round de room an' round de room, casting one spell dat anybody who use dat name again dey dwop down dead dat minute. . . ."

"Roun' de room an' roun' de room an' roun' de room," said Titty to herself, counting with a finger as she said it. "Three times round. That's easy enough. And the cave ought to be a good enough room to do it in."

She had trouble over the making of the image, even

though she did not try to make a very good one. Candle-grease is not wax and the able-seaman soon found that she could do nothing with it unless it was warm and almost liquid. She had nothing to warm it in except the mate's cooking pans. She did not much like using them, but decided that to save anybody's mother from a great-aunt of this kind it would be right to use anything, and anyhow it would soon be over and she would be able to get the frying-pan (which seemed to be the best shape for melting candle-grease) clean and shiny again before Susan came back from Swainson's farm.

She remembered that before frying anything the mate always put a little butter in the pan, so that nothing should stick to it. It was a good thing she remembered that, she thought, and by the time she had put the butter in the frying-pan and was warming it over the fire she felt as if she had been doing this kind of cooking all her life. As soon as the butter was properly melted and sizzling on the bottom of the pan she broke up the slab of candle-grease and dropped the bits in and tilted the pan first one way and then the other until the bits all melted and ran together. There seemed to be very little candle-grease to make an image of. She got the other three lanterns out of the tents. There was only a stub of a candle-end in each, and there were plenty of new candles in one of the tin boxes. So she put the three candle-ends into the frying pan with the stuff that was there already, added a little more butter and warmed it up again until, as she tilted the pan, the candle-grease poured round like thick sauce. Then, of course, the trouble was that it was too hot. She had to wait for it to cool. But the moment it was cool enough, she began scraping it up with a spoon, and presently had a good big lump of candle-grease, not quite too hot to touch, and was

kneading it between her hands and keeping it moving
from one hand to the other as if it were a hot potato.

She turned it quickly into a great-aunt. There was a
small round blob for a head ("It's no good trying to do
snaky hair") stuck on a long straight body, rolled between
her hands, plumped down on a stone and made to stand
upright, and then pinched in a little at the middle. The
arms, too, were made separately and then stuck on. She
scraped a little more candle-grease from round the edge of
the frying-pan and used it to make two feet. They were not
a success, so she squashed them together and made them
into a hat instead, pressing it down on the blob that was
meant for a head. There was no time to do much model-
ling. The candle-grease hardened too quickly as it cooled.
Anyhow, it was horrid to touch, but that, perhaps, was
partly the fault of the butter. She gave the thing eyes,
marking them in with a charred and blackened stick from
the edge of the fire, and she scratched a slit of a mouth
somewhere below the place where she would have liked
to make a nose if the candle-grease had still been soft
enough.

The frying-pan smelt as nasty as it looked. There was no
time to lose if it was to be cleaned and polished before the
others came back. So Titty borrowed Susan's torch out of
her tent and hurried into the cave to get on with the spell.

She set the torch on the ground in the middle of the
cave, pointing upwards so that it lit the roof, and then,
holding the candle-grease doll before her, she walked three
times round the cave, talking to the image as she walked.

"*Be* the great-aunt! *Be* the great-aunt! *Be* the great-
aunt!"

Then, catching her breath, she ran hurriedly out into the
sunlight. It was a comfort, after that, to see that the parrot

had gone back into his cage and was eating a lump of sugar as if nothing special was going on.

The great-aunt, smelling horribly, now felt somehow different to her fingers. Had she really found the right spell? She almost wished the others would come back before anything else happened. Then she remembered what Nancy had said about Mrs Blackett crying and she bit her teeth sharply together. She was not going to stop now.

But the question was, what, exactly, ought she to do? It would be no good just pushing pins into the great-aunt's legs and arms, or into her body, because if something went wrong with a leg or an arm, or if she were seriously ill, the great-aunt would be sure to stay at Beckfoot and be horrible to everybody until she felt better. Besides, perhaps it was true that only a real silver pin would be any good. What she wanted was just to make the great-aunt thoroughly uncomfortable, so that she would want to go away. Titty looked doubtfully at the image. If she rolled the image in the dust would it mean that the real great-aunt, away at Beckfoot, would suddenly throw herself on the ground and begin rolling about? That would be most worrying for Mrs Blackett.

Then she remembered reading in the book how the native wizards when they make the wax image of an enemy melt it slowly over a fire, and believe that as the image melts away so does their enemy loose strength until at last, when the whole image is melted, he dies.

Of course, the thing would be to melt the image just a very little, not enough to make the great-aunt ill, but just enough to make her feel not quite herself, and that she would be better in a more bracing air. Then she would pack her boxes and go away and everybody would be perfectly happy.

She held out the candle-grease doll over the fire. Nothing happened except that the hand in which she was holding it grew very hot long before the doll seemed to feel the heat at all. Then she changed hands again and this time, perhaps because she took hold of a part of the image that had been nearest to the heat, perhaps because the wood shifted and a little flame licked up and burnt her fingers, perhaps just because the candle-grease was melting and slippery (how it was she could never explain to herself) the thing was gone, her fingers closed on nothing, there was a dreadful spluttering in the fire, yellow smoky flames shot up and a moment later, though Titty scattered the sticks in all directions trying to save her, no one could have told that a great-aunt had ever been there at all.

Titty's first thought was that there would never be time to make another. But the next moment she had thought of something else, and no longer an able-seaman, no longer even a Negro witch, she burst into horrified tears.

"I didn't mean to kill her," she wailed. "I really didn't."

She saw the great-aunt at Beckfoot, stricken suddenly, gasping for breath, dead. She saw Nancy and Peggy running along the lake road not knowing that when they came home they would find the blinds down in the windows of the house. Would they guess at once what she had done? What would they think? Even Nancy would think it was too much. It was all very well for the scuppers of a pirate ship to run with blood. This was different. The great-aunt dead, and dead in such a manner, was worse than the great-aunt alive even if she made Mrs Blackett miserable and was spoiling the Amazon's holidays. And she had done it. She felt as if she had tried to ring the bell quietly at the door of a big house and the bell was going on pealing and pealing as if it would never stop.

"I wish I'd never thought of it. But I didn't mean to kill her. I didn't. All I wanted was for her to go to the seaside."

"Pretty Polly. Pretty Polly," said the ship's parrot, who had come to the end of his bit of sugar and was wondering if he had any chance of getting another.

Titty looked at him through her tears, and wondered suddenly if she had truly done anything at all. Had she just planned to make a great-aunt and to cast a spell. . . ? She had often planned things until they seemed quite as real. But when she wiped her face with her hands she felt the smudge of sooty candle-grease. She saw the frying-pan waiting to be cleaned . . . the empty lanterns . . . No. There was no doubt about it. The thing had really happened.

Just then the others came climbing up into Swallowdale.

"A farmer's cart gave them a lift," shouted the ship's boy.

"They're going to be awfully late just the same," said John grimly. "I wish they hadn't waited for the hound-trail. Hullo, Titty, whatever's the matter?"

"What have you been doing to the fire?" said Susan, "and the frying pan? And the lanterns? And what have you got on your face?"

"Roger, go and get some more wood out of Peter Duck's," said Captain John. "There's some just inside the door."

The moment the boy had gone into the cave, Titty poured out the dreadful truth.

"I've done it," she said, "but I didn't mean to kill her. She slipped in my fingers and got melted and burnt up."

"Who did?" asked John.

"The great-aunt," said Titty. "I made her out of candle-grease and I meant to melt her just a very little, but she slipped."

"Well, you can easily make another," said John.

"But she's dead," said Titty. "They'll find she's dead when they get back to Beckfoot and they'll know it's my fault."

"Rubbish, Titty," said Susan. "She's perfectly all right and scolding them like anything. All you've done is to make a dirty mess of a clean frying-pan. Go and wash your face and clean the frying-pan while I crack the eggs into a mug. I promised Roger I'd scramble them."

"Look here, Titty," said John. "It isn't as if you'd had the proper wax, and even if you had you'd have had to burn it on purpose if you were going to do any good. Just dropping it in the fire by accident means nothing at all."

Roger came out of the cave with an armful of wood and Susan's torch.

"I found it in the middle of the floor," he said. "It's gone very dim."

"I'm most awfully sorry," said Titty. "I forgot it when I was casting the spell."

"What spell?" asked John.

"Going round and round three times," said Titty.

"Go and clean the frying-pan," said Susan, "and let's have supper."

Susan built up the scattered fire and soon there was once more a cheerful blaze. Scrubbing the frying-pan made Titty feel rather better, and though at supper the scrambled eggs did taste a little of candle-grease, just eating her share of them by the fire with the others was enough to make black magic seem unreal.

But late that night Susan heard Titty stir uneasily in her tent. Susan wriggled a hand out from under her tent and into Titty's which was close beside it. Titty found the hand and held it tight.

"I didn't mean to kill her," she whispered.

"Of course you didn't and you haven't," said Susan.

"We'll know in the morning."

"We know now," said Susan. "Go to sleep."

The Downfall of Witches

THE DANGERS OF SORCERY

ISAIAH

Nearly all witch stories have one feature in common. In the end, the witch is defeated.

To the Hebrew prophet and poet who wrote this passage from The Book of the Prophet Isaiah, *the downfall of those who trust in sorcery is a cause for rejoicing. William Butler Yeats takes a different view. He was an Irishman, whom many people consider was the greatest poet writing in English in the twentieth century. In his* Lines Written in Dejection *he sees the downfall of witches as the end of magic and beauty.*

Therefore hear now this, thou that art given to pleasures,
    that dwellest carelessly,
That sayest in thine heart, "I am, and none else beside me;
I shall not sit as a widow, neither shall I know the loss of
    children:"
But these two things shall come to thee in a moment of
    one day,
The loss of children and widowhood:
They shall come upon thee in their perfection
For the multitude of thy sorceries, and for the great
    abundance of thine enchantments.
For thou hast trusted in thy wickedness: thou hast said,
    "None seeth me."

Thy wisdom and thy knowledge, it hath perverted thee;

And thou hast said in thine heart, "I am, and none else beside me."

Therefore shall evil come upon thee; thou shalt not know from whence it riseth:

And mischief shall fall upon thee; thou shalt not be able to put it off:

And desolation shall come upon thee suddenly, which thou shalt not know.

Stand now with thine enchantments and with the multitude of thy sorceries,

Wherein thou hast laboured from thy youth;

If so be thou shalt be able to profit, if so be thou mayest prevail.

Thou art wearied in the multitude of thy counsels.

Let now the astrologers, the stargazers, the monthly prognosticators,

Stand up and save thee from these things that shall come upon thee.

Behold they shall be as stubble; the fire shall burn them;

They shall not deliver themselves from the power of the flame:

There shall not be a coal to warm at, nor fire to sit before it.

Thus shall they be unto thee with whom thou hast laboured, even thy merchants, from thy youth:

They shall wander every one to his quarter; none shall save thee.

LINES WRITTEN IN DEJECTION

W. B. YEATS

When have I last looked on
The round green eyes and the long wavering bodies
Of the dark leopards of the moon?
All the wild witches, those most noble ladies,
For all their broom-sticks and their tears,
Their angry tears, are gone.
The holy centaurs of the hills are vanished;
I have nothing but the embittered sun;
Banished heroic mother moon and vanished.
And now that I am come to fifty years
I must endure the timid sun.

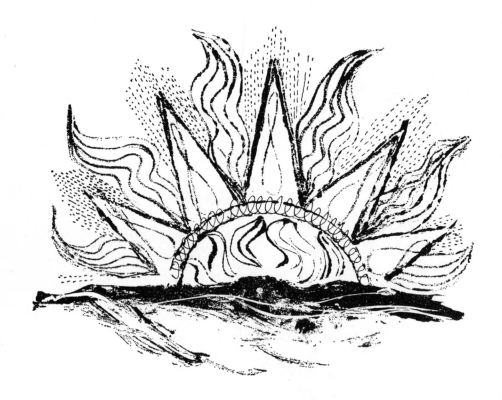